# THE SCHOOL WE HAVE

How Troubled,
Fed-up Adolescents
Get Together with
Creative Adults at **THE**

# SCHOOL WE HAVE

*Shepard Ginandes, M.D.*

Delacorte Press / Seymour Lawrence

Ginandes, Shepard, 1928-
How troubled, fed-up adolescents get together with creative adults at The School We Have.

Bibliography: p.
1. The School We Have.  2. Problem children—Education—United States.  3. Gifted children—Education—United States.  4. Psychotherapy.  I. Title.
II. Title: The School We Have.
LD7501.C78G5      371'.02'0973      72-8391

Copyright © 1973 by Shepard Ginandes, M.D.
All rights reserved. No part of this book may be reproduced in any form or by any means without the prior written permission of the Publisher, excepting brief quotes used in connection with reviews written specifically for inclusion in a magazine or newspaper.
Manufactured in the United States of America
Designed by Judith Lerner Thiesen
First printing

I WANT TO EXPRESS my deepest gratitude to those young people who have come to me over the years and showed me what they needed in order to grow up whole. They have been the ones who made me see the need for the School We Have. Their parents have also helped me understand the problem of individuation and identity formation in depth, and I want to thank those parents who went through the pains of family therapy and letting their kids grow up in their own way.

It is hard to thank the staff of the School sufficiently. Early staff members like Dick Stroud, June Judson, Mary Till, David Maxwell, Magdelyn Hayes, Pat Prencipe, and Marcia Cardillo worked creatively under hard conditions to establish the unique atmosphere of our School. So did later teachers: Linda Bates, Roger Gregoire, Carol Beckwith, Dick Lerman, David Barker, Jon Matson, and Sensei Mitsunari Kanai. Student teachers like Carl Cascella, Lisa Swallow, Claudia Bunyard, and Jerry Lipschutz have shared their developing skills, too.

The School's amazing therapy capability has been thanks to therapists Bob and Ildri Ginn, Dick Goldwater, Henry Schniewind and Natalie Fuchs.

My gratitude goes out to Reverend Nigel Andrews and the staff of Trinity Episcopal Church in Concord, who gave the School a home when we needed it most.

Special gratitude to Gregory Bateson, who cured me of a

writer's block on page 2, and thanks to David Manning White, who listened patiently as this manuscript evolved from an idea into a book.

TO LOIS

*my wife and codirector of the School
whose loving partnership made the School possible*

# Contents

**PART 1  Introduction**  1

1  Lonely Shrinks, Lonely Parents  3
2  Where Did It Go?  7

**PART 2  The School We Have**  17

3  What We Do at the School  19
4  Saturday at the School We Have  42
5  Kids  70
6  Teachers  93
7  What Happens in Classes at the School  111
8  Group Therapy: Finding Openness  139
9  Individual Therapy: To Recover the Wholeness  149
10  The Divine Self: Yoga and Meditation at the School  163

## PART 3 Somebody Knows What Is Best for You    165

    11   Adolescent Psychiatry as Transcultural Psychiatry    169
    12   The Question of Authority    184
    13   Families I: The Clash of Values    192
    14   Families II: The Declaration of Personhood    209
    15   Drugs and Creative Kids    229

## PART 4 Conclusion: "I Am What I Am, But Not Yet"    241

    16   So Far    243
    17   Dynamics    256

    *Bibliography*    263

# THE SCHOOL WE HAVE

# PART 1 ›
# Introduction

# 1 › Lonely Shrinks, Lonely Parents

WHO IS THIS BOOK FOR? Who needs to hear about an experiment in relating with "alienated" adolescents, and what use can anyone make of the story? Publishers asked me these questions. And then I asked myself. But recently across America at least one of the answers has begun to appear. All over, new kinds of schools have sprung up—free schools, Summerhill schools, nonschools. Educators are getting worried about their failure to reach and motivate adolescents, whether in public, private, or parochial schools, and parents are getting worried about leaving their children's education to pedagogues.

Similar doubts and concerns have gripped our mental health professionals. How effective with adolescents is our Freudian-based psychotherapy in the office or clinic? These concerned professionals are beginning to violate the precepts of their training in psychiatric residency or what they learned in graduate school about psychology and psychiatric social work. They are trying out group and family therapy, teams of therapists, sensitivity training and encounter groups, and now therapeutic communities. And in regional mental health clinics and state hospitals, private psychiatric facilities, and encounter centers we are now seeing younger and more active therapists, impatient with the old dogmas. Here and there it has become impossible to tell the therapist from the patients without an ID badge, and this may be a very good thing indeed for the patient, in a lot of ways.

Meanwhile, in communes and pads all over the country, young people who are fed up with the ways of society are banding together to live. They are dreaming of new-style "families" that will replace the old nuclear families they came from—father, mother, and two and a half kids in a city apartment or suburban split-level home. One young visionary I met is about to establish a "family" in Hawaii—he is looking for a big house. People will be able to come there to live, alone or in couples or groups, and share the responsibilities of the house and of daily life. "I don't want to be daddy or to have authority. But we need some way to deal with people's feelings and the emotional situations that come up. Maybe a regular encounter group—some way to keep communicating with each other. . . ." he wonders. What is he looking for? Why go to all that trouble? He is looking for what most of us are looking for: a life that feels good in the here and now, but one that moves toward some goal or purpose, some direction we respect. Whether that purpose is making art or helping people or improving our environment or finding out about something, we want to find our purpose and serve it each in our own style with the least interference and the most help from the world around us. If we are honest with ourselves, we find out that kids and adults have these same objectives in life.

But if adults and kids want the same things from life, why can't they get together? We tried it and it works. This book is the story of how we tried it and how it works. And it is written to help others realize that life can reach these goals, that adults can learn to help kids design their own lives and live their own way. So this book is for people who want to set up new kinds of situations between adults and adolescents—situations for relating, for education, and for therapy. The list of people who became involved in our project is long—it includes kids, teachers, artists, musicians, ministers, doctors, psychiatrists, psychologists and social workers, parents, probation officers and lawyers, and more. In short, our experiment involved the kinds of people who live in any community.

Before this project began I was a lonely shrink. I knew that something was wrong with the techniques I had learned in my training. Techniques of psychoanalytically oriented psychotherapy focus upon making the patient reveal himself, but never the therapist. I have since met many other lonely shrinks and mental health professionals, all wondering why the system fails to reach adolescents generally and how to change it. How far do you go? How close can you get? How much do you reveal of your own life and your concerns? Our project has suggested answers to some of these vital questions. So to the lonely shrinks and other mental health pros, this book is specially dedicated.

And what about the lonely fifteen-year-olds who feel so turned off by school and their tired teachers? Surely, they figure, teaching should be more than just another way of making money. And when they turn toward their parents they so often find there too a sense of fatigue and joylessness in the roles of husband, wife, father, and mother. It is so rare to find a turned-on, excited adult who clearly enjoys his life —and when these kids don't find such adults at home or at school, too often they begin to feel the game is rigged; you can't survive in society and remain alive. As one fifteen-year-old girl put it, "If you're not living, you're not alive." So to the lonely fifteen-year-olds still hoping to encounter adults turned on by life, this book is also dedicated.

I am hoping the chronicle of how we conducted our project and made our School will also help the turned-on people who are making schools and communes and halfway houses for kids. Possibly the story of our successes and our mistakes will help them stick with it and build new and stronger bridges between the generations.

Parents are lonely too. Finding that the lessons they learned so laboriously in life are ignored or rejected by their teen-age children, finding themselves regarded as old-fashioned and their advice irrelevant to "life today," parents don't know whether to retreat to authority positions or to abandon their adolescents entirely. "Don't expect any help from me if you are caught taking drugs," or, "How do I know what this kid is doing? He never comes home except for food and money!" One of the most distressing aspects of adolescent life today is the great gulf of communication and understanding on everything vital between so many kids and their parents. If parents could be encouraged by what they read here to learn a new style of communication with their adolescents, at least some nonfamilies could begin to function like families once again.

In 1968 we founded our School with five kids and three teachers and one psychiatrist. After regular school hours, evenings and Saturdays, we did art, music, dance, and drama together and learned how group therapy can work with adults and "alienated" kids together. New students and teachers joined us. We grew and soon we survived our first crisis, having to move the School. We moved into a basement of an Episcopal church. A kind minister and his staff had saved us from possible extinction. Now at maximum size, we are sixty students, twenty-two teachers, and two shrinks, and we have learned a lot. Our School is known as the School We Have.

We did not proceed from theory to practice. We started with three inputs of energy and ideas: my own psychiatric training and views, the ideas of a group of bright and creative kids who had lots of experience in the wrong kinds of schools and therapies, and the exciting improvisations of a group of turned-on teachers, most of them artists, most of them sick of working under the limitations imposed by public and private high schools and colleges. In the following chapters I will try to describe what we found out and how it fits and doesn't fit into existing theories of work with adolescents.

# 2 › Where Did It Go?

NOT LONG AGO I heard a young anthropologist describe the life style of a tribe in New Guinea. He had spent over a year there doing a field study and living with a small tribe of people who inhabit a remote valley. He had learned their language and he loved them. As he spoke, a picture emerged of a style of living shared by everyone in the tribe, some five hundred people. They raise pigs and vegetables. Every so often they accumulate enough pigs to hold a festival, in which they slaughter the pigs and dedicate them to the spirits of their departed ancestors. Naturally, a large number of pigs are needed in order to do sufficient honor to the spirits, who might otherwise be displeased and cause trouble for the tribe. After the pigs are dedicated and their flesh eaten, battles against neighboring tribes, which have been suspended before the festival, are once more possible. Nobody fights with anybody while a festival is in preparation. As the story unfolded, I got the picture of an endless cycle of food increase and population growth, then small wars and population decrease. All phases of life, including festivals and wars, are related to pleasing the spirits of the ancestors, which are the gods. Over the centuries the ways of life and death in that tiny community have not changed much. The population has remained nearly constant for many decades.

What I was hearing about was a society living under cybernetic control; when it gets too large and the food supply becomes insufficient, this society has its traditional ways of reducing its population. When the population decreases, there is more food available and the society can grow again. This is no paradise: conditions are hard, and people do not live long. But nothing is out of control. Life and death, food supply and population, nature and art and religion are kept in balance by the way everyone lives every day. Whatever a tribesman does is bound up with all other aspects of the life style of his tribe. A "participation mystique," McLuhan would call it. Each aspect of life, including nature, in its place and all fitting together. This sense of harmony and balance in primitive societies has been described by many anthropologists, including Colin Turnbull in *The Forest People* and is beautifully described by Tobias Schneebaum in *Keep the River on Your Right*.

As I listened to the story of that small world, I began to think about the lives of the adolescents who are my patients in Boston, America, today. I realized that what is missing in their lives and mine is precisely that which is so much present in the valleys of New Guinea—the certainty, the inevitability of a rhythmic cycle of life. Our lives cannot be predicted, we cannot count on anything but death. And even *how* and *when* we will die has changed in the past few years. Our lives are running away with us. They are strange to us. Our parents did not live as we do, and our children will not live as we do either. We are unfamiliar with the conditions of our childrens' lives, no matter how hard we try to make them consistent. Parents cannot take back the H-bomb, the pointless cold and hot wars, the mass media, the automobile, air and water pollution. We must bring up our children in a world which has run away from us, become strange to us.

Just as the world is changing and running away, so are the young people who must grow up in it. Twenty-year-olds in America are shocked at the behavior of seventeen-year-olds. The pace of change is increasing all the time. Older and younger people in America 1970 are no longer bound together by a common heritage of life experience. When traditional and respected ways of dealing with life situations are abandoned, we also give up the spiritual and aesthetic satisfactions of those ways. If a New Guinea native stops carving shields for battle because galvanized iron garbage-can lids are now cheap and easily available, he also gives up a particular religious-aesthetic experience that bound him to the life style of his people throughout time. We have lost this organic relationship with the religious and aesthetic aspects of our lives. Art and nature and religion are no longer central in the life of Americans, particularly the middle class. We indulge in art, visit nature, practice religion self-consciously, but they are no longer essential parts of our everyday living.

It takes time, generations of familiarity with his environment, for man to invest this environment with meaning. In time, under unchanged conditions, men everywhere find significance in nature, in the human condition. Life and death and all the events and crises of life are worked into systems of religious belief and expressed in art. When the conditions of life change too rapidly, it becomes harder and harder to build a complete human adaptation into such a changing environment. How can you set out to build the walls of the city or Notre Dame Cathedral or to carve a ceremonial shield when tomorrow your tools and materials will be out of date, and when, the day after, the enabling concepts by which you worked will be archaic. What we have lost, among other things, is *time*. Time to make our lives within our environment meaningful to ourselves and our children. However narrow-minded our ancestors might have been, they had time to develop a life style which made living meaningful, which sanctified human existence, and which could be taught to their children.

Human beings seem to need the kind of very deep thinking-feeling that accompanies involvement with nature, art, and religion. Whether you call it mystical or transcendental experience, primary process, or peak experience, it is a state of being we cannot live without. When we don't find this state of being naturally in the course of our lives we must search for it. A person deprived of sleep suffers "dream deprivation." After awhile he dreams while half awake. He *must* dream to keep intact his mind and spirit. In just this way, states of being representing deep harmony with nature, beauty and the spiritual are *vital* to man. When they do not come spontaneously with the living of life, we must create them.

It is these very states of being that young people today are trying desperately to find. Middle-class American adolescents, in particular, are probably of all people on earth the most deprived of nature, art, ritual, and religion in their day-to-day lives. Feeling intuitively a terrible emptiness and meaninglessness in life, they have begun to experiment with ways to reinvest life with the sense of meaning that comes naturally to the New Guinea native as he slaughters the pig and offers the blood to the spirits of his ancestors, as he plants the special plant that means "festival," even as he and his comrades work themselves up for a postfestival struggle against the warriors from the next village. So our teen-agers shuffle to the fantastically loud music that drives their parents from the house. They paint their bodies, wear far-out clothing, create drug sacraments. What they are reaching for is process, it is context. They know unconsciously that what we have lost from our lives is sanctification. Whatever we do these days tends to be out of context, done for *result*, for *product*, and ends up dividing us, making us less whole. And we are *all* suffering from the disease of not being whole, parents and children alike. With the increasing rate of technological "progress" whoever is born last will suffer the most as environment becomes still less whole, still more fragmented and alienating. It is no accident that those most fascinated with psychedelic drugs are the fifteen- and sixteen-year-olds. "Tripping" means to them being *fully involved*, caught up in something all the way down to your roots. They do not find their parents and teachers so involved in what *they* are doing, and most of them have never known an adult who is deeply and passionately involved in the *process* of his own life. When, for the first time, perhaps under LSD or mescaline, they find that feeling of full immersion in experience, it is a revelation. And lacking the personal skills and the life experience to create this experience naturally, many find the drug route to be the easiest way. A fifteen-year-old girl put it this way: "I only feel alive when I am completely involved. And I just can't seem to feel that way in school or at home. I hear you can train yourself to get into that state through zen or yoga or meditation, but that takes *years*. With acid, you get there in twenty minutes." It is absolutely undeniable that thousands of young people *have* gotten there in twenty minutes with these drugs. The problem is not how to get there, it is how to make that beautiful state a part of *everyday* life. And more and more young people are refusing to follow those of their elders who do not appear to have found a way. According to what I have been told by hundreds of adolescent seekers, the list of those elders who have not found a way to participate fully in the process of life includes most parents, most teachers, and most psychotherapists. The parents and teachers and therapists of middle-class American kids have become:

>Wealthy
>Busy
>Tired
>Lonely
>Product-oriented
>Responsible
>Joyless

Many adolescents, equating the emptiness of spirit and the way of life of their elders, have taken the obvious step of trying to live the *reverse* of their parents' lives. For work, substitute passivity. For business, pot and inertia. They try to be always available for living in the moment, whatever might arise. But they themselves do not make anything arise. If your father appears to be a robot in his job, if your parents appear unloving in their marriage, why go to the trouble of creating an imitation of their lives? Maybe by doing the opposite of what they do, you can avoid their feeling of tired emptiness, maybe you can find the answer. But you can't—not that way. And in many a discotheque, between the sets when the music is momentarily stilled, as I walk through the shadows and observe the costumed children squatting passively and empty-faced along the walls and in the corners, waiting for something to happen, I feel strongly that this is not the *answer* either. There is little joy, little happiness among those who are trying to live the negative of the standard, middle-class American life. Avoiding a wrong road does not automatically put you on a right one.

Here and there a voice is heard that puts us on the track of an answer. A neurophysiologist says: "Science is just an attempt to learn something. What teaches is when you get stuck yourself and you get your students to help you out of it." An ecologist told me: "I have to let my students see that I'm up against it, too, just like they are. We share, my students and I, the same real human predicaments." And a communications researcher told me: "In the universities, Shakespeare and mathematics have been chopped out of context. The essence of relating is *context*—if you are my close friend, I know what *you* mean by Shakespeare. When the relationship between student and teacher loses context, it becomes anonymous. The greats like Shakespeare and Sophocles are relevant by their *process*, not by their products."

These statements come close to what R. D. Laing means in his fascinating book *The Politics of Experience*, when he defines psychotherapy this way:

"Psychotherapy must remain *an obstinate attempt of two people to recover the wholeness of being human through the relationship between them.*"

In my view, *any* relationship between people to be worth anything at all must recover the wholeness of being human. And too often in the name of "protecting the children" parents also protect themselves from revealing the realness, the *context* of their own deepest feelings. All of us, wrapped in the environment we have helped to create, have lost too much of the wholeness of being human. Our young people perceive this. We must not blame them for not wanting to follow suit. Can we still help them? Can we show them where minefields lie buried, and the ditches and the crevasses that stopped us?

At our school we learned that we can—if we will be *open* and fully human with our patients and our students. The hard part is, of course, that in order to be yourself with others you must be willing to be yourself with yourself. This book documents an attempt to develop a new and more fully human relationship between some already "alienated" American adolescents and a few older people. These adults include psychiatrists, an actress, a dancer, two printers, a couple of musicians, a writer, an astrologer, and others. Some of these people are married, half have children. Some are living a "straight life," as the kids define it. Others have resisted a full-time job, marriage, owning a car and a house. All share with our students the common occupation of seeker. We are trying to do in our lives what means the most to us, and we are seeking ways to do it better. We are willing to share with the kids our life stories and our human feelings, our successes and failures. What we are doing comes much closer to Laing's definition of psychotherapy than to Freud's or anyone else's. We are trying to recover the wholeness of being human in our relationship with the young people who come to us. As a result, our definition of success can not be simply whether this or that adolescent leaves us and gets a job and goes to college. He may or may not. But if he leaves more able to experience the wholeness of his humanity, we have succeeded.

Essentially, then, what are we trying to do? Therapy, unquestionably, but what ailment are we treating and for what purpose? Working with the adolescent children of America's affluent middle class, the offspring of suburbia, we find ourselves learning the epidemiology of affluence and upward mobility. And we treat the complications that arise from affluence and upward mobility:

> The feeling that life is meaningless.
> The feeling that education and jobs are irrelevant.
> A disinterest in "success" as defined by parents.
> A lack of understanding of what is to be gained from work.
> A lack of understanding of what is to be gained from human relationships.

In a New Guinea tribe or any tradition-governed society, there are agreed-upon *reasons* for what everybody does. "He kills the pig to feed the spirits of his ancestors." "She wears an amulet on her breast to ward off disease." "He visits his grandfather to show respect." It is not so much *what* is done, but that it is done for a purpose, a purpose shared by the other members of the tribe or the community. The agreed-upon purpose *sanctifies* the act which is performed, makes it the right thing to do. In middle-class America, the tremendous noisy input of advice and example poured into the eyes and ears of every child by parents, teachers, friends, TV, radio, LP records and magazines shows the child that there is no *right* thing to do, there are a hundred alternative things to do, most of them conflicting. And even the new edict "do your thing" doesn't tell you what is right to do. As one boy said, "I'm ready to do my thing but I don't know what my thing is." Still another told me, "I don't know any of the answers. I don't even know the questions."

How do you find out what your thing is? Does it come to you in a vision, in a dream? Is it whatever gives pleasure? If so then many people's thing is pot-smoking and casual sex. But they soon get tired of these and look for a more fully

*Introduction*

satisfying thing. In the program we designed, the program this book is about, young people study painting, drama, jazz and blues and rock music and so on with older people who have found their thing. Each of these teachers have found something to do, something which makes them whole and unites them with life in the largest sense. They are not all totally happy or satisfied people. But their lives have meaning to them—each knows that he is doing the *right* thing for him—perhaps the only thing he can imagine doing. And each has made some relationship with society whereby his work is accepted and he can continue working. Each of these teachers is convinced of the meaning and importance of what he is doing. This feeling is the cement of life; without it, there are only bricks, fragments, heaps of rubble.

Our complex society officially sanctifies only certain kinds of activities for its young people—going to school, getting a job. Our educational system is set up from the very beginning to funnel our children systematically toward the roles that the society wants filled—those and no others. Increasingly, young people, particularly the creative ones, are finding that what parents and teachers want them to do with their lives does not feel right to *them*. And what feels right to them (if it is art, music, dance, drama, and so on) does not meet with the approval of parents and teachers. By the time they are in high school, bright open-minded young people realize they are in conforming school. Edgar Z. Friedenberg documents this strikingly in his book *Coming of Age in America*. Yet they are aware of so many other ways to live. What they have read, seen in the movies and on TV has once and for all made these adolescents aware that there are infinite ways to spend your life. Knowing how people live all over the world is a phenomenon of our century alone. Modern communication has reached the point where anything that happens almost anywhere in the world can be seen "live" in any American living room the same day. If you take your child on a walk through your local toy store, he will want what he sees there.

The wise parent avoids doing that unless he intends to buy the child a toy. But our adolescents are exposed nowadays to a fantastic amount of information—true, false, and distorted —about how people live, about pleasures and rewards he might choose for himself. Still the pressure from most parents and educators can be summed up in the words of one father: "I hope my son gets all this searching for truth out of his system so he can settle down and get into a good business!"

The sense of rightness and meaning in the few human activities pursued by simple society is gone from our lives. The cement once furnished by the society to bind together all human activity into a meaningful whole is no longer supplied. The feeling of rightness that sanctifies human endeavour must come from the individual. He must find in himself the strength to push through all barriers until he finds a style of life that makes him whole. No one else can do it for him, but older people who have taken that same road can be immensely valuable to him. They can show him that it *can* be done, it *has* been done, and that the techniques for doing it can be learned. In the light of the confusion and widespread despair in our society, the apprenticeship of an adolescent seeking wholeness to an older teacher more experienced in the same quest can be of vital importance. It can be a keystone in his identity formation, a critical and formative experience. One of the main things we learned at the School was how to bring kids and such teachers together in ways that encourage a mutual apprenticeship. Our students and teachers share with one another the techniques for living authentic creative lives.

# PART 2 ›
# The School We Have

# 3 › What We Do at the School

IN MASLOW's wonderful book *Toward a Psychology of Being*, he says:

> . . . Growth takes place when the next step forward is subjectively more delightful, more joyous, more intrinsically satisfying than the last; the only way we can ever know what is right for us is that it feels better subjectively than any alternative. The new experience validates *itself* rather than by any outside criterion. It is self-justifying, self-validating.
>
> We don't do it because it is good for us, or because psychologists approve, or because somebody told us to, or because it will make us live longer, or because it is good for the species, or because it will bring external rewards, or because it is logical. We do it for the same reason that we choose one dessert over another. . . .

I have never been lucky enough to attend a school where this sort of growth Maslow describes was paramount. Doing what *others* felt was right was always what school demanded of me, from penmanship to giving up singing. But school and learning situations don't *have* to be this way. As a result of experiencing and finally rejecting the "play it safe" kind of schools, I realized that a learning and growing environment for young people should be different. I designed a new program—the sort of place where an adolescent can find the greatest encouragement to do what feels right to *him*. Here young people can experiment with their *own* choices and styles, whatever they are. In such an environment, young people are most likely to overcome internal barriers to growth; they begin to feel safe in reaching out and *trying* things.

One of my main goals in setting up a new kind of therapy for young people was to see if together we could create an environment in which we could help each other find a way to grow through uncovering not only our difficulties (which is the orientation of standard psychotherapy) but our capacity for *making* full, enjoyable, and meaningful lives as each of us design them for ourselves. I will tell you the story of the kind of therapeutic community we built together and how it works.

After setting up this community, I read Margaret Mead's fascinating book *Culture and Commitment,* and I discovered what to call what we have been doing. I have been working with adolescents in a new *cocognitive* culture, to use her term. What she describes is our present situation in which parents and children must learn from *each other.* No longer can parents lead their children into lives similar to their own, because the world in which our children have grown up is an entirely different world from that in which their parents grew up, and *neither* parents nor children yet know how to live in it. The old lessons no longer apply. The best that can be done is to admit that none of us, old or young, know how to live well in our new environment, and then to pool our ideas on how we might find out. But this kind of discussion as *equals* takes place in very few homes. So we created a school, a cocognitive mini-culture, in which older and younger people could enter deeply into this kind of dialogue and learn from each other. Our students decided to call it "the School We Have," and the name stuck.

Maslow describes in *Toward a Psychology of Being* how such an environment encourages growth:

... we can learn important lessons from the therapy situation, the creative educative situation, creative art education and I believe also creative dance education. Here where the situation is set up variously as permissive, admiring, praising, accepting, safe, gratifying, reassuring, supporting, unthreatening, non-valuing, non-comparing, that is where the person can feel completely safe and unthreatened, then it becomes possible for him to work out and express all sorts of lesser delights, e.g., hostility, neurotic dependency. Once these are sufficiently catharted, he then tends spontaneously to go onto other delights which outsiders perceive to be "higher" or growthward, e.g., love, creativeness, and which he himself will prefer to the previous delights, once he has experienced them both.

Any environment is the sum of the spirits of the people who make it. I wanted to create an environment in which adolescents could feel safe enough to express the archaic feelings that fill them with fear of themselves and make them feel unsafe to grow. This would have to be a place where anger, jealousy, clinging dependency, fear of rejection, and a conviction of inferiority could be expressed, tolerated, understood, and finally drained of emotional energy to the point where these problems would no longer prevent movement forward toward love and creativeness. We would need a special kind of teacher, people who could tolerate and understand these feelings. But I was not anxious to create a merely "therapeutic" scene. I did not want the emphasis in the minds of creative arts teachers to be upon the regressive feelings that *block* creativity and love, I did *not* set about to find people who had training or experience as *therapists*. I looked for *artists*. Artists because (as Maslow pointed out) artists know that what is important is what the person himself has to say. Artists put the emphasis on the message coming from *inside* us and use artistic techniques to get the message across. Yet I also wanted a special kind of artist—someone who had battled with the regressive forces in his or her personality at some time and had come out on top. These teachers would have to be people who had experienced the same pull of forces that tend to hold back kids from the developing of a Self—the same angers, fears, and dependencies that I have fought against, that everyone seeking self-actualization must fight against. These would be people each of whom *has* found an authentic Self, people who live it every day. As Maslow says,

> Only the one who respects fear and defense can teach; only the one who respects health can do therapy.

In a later chapter I reveal how in my own life, I had to struggle against amputation of the Self. All around us young people are struggling against this same danger. ("Strike because they are squeezing the life out of you!") It was therefore my prime concern that our teachers should each be a living example that the Self can live, surviving all snares and traps. No matter who wanted them to be different or who found them unacceptable, they had come out themselves.

We started off by finding these teachers. Our program developed around the teachers who lived up to this high qualification of authenticity. In our first year this turned out to include:

> Drama—acting, spontaneous improvisation.
> Dance movement—the body communicating feelings.
> Yoga—body development, relaxation training.
> Meditation—mystical experience, "turning on" without drugs.
> Creative writing—getting the message across in written words.
> Painting, sculpture, mixed media—saying it visually.
> Basic music group—playing music together, feeling safe

to express yourself with an instrument and share the experience.

Piano instruction (individual)—emphasis on technique to help you say what *you* want to say (jazz, blues, etc.).

Classes met all day Saturday and Wednesday afternoon and evening. That has remained our schedule except for yoga and meditation class, which meets Friday afternoon. Over half our students attend other schools simultaneously with ours, so our schedule accommodates them.

For our first year and a half the School was located in a studio building deep in the woods on my property. Almost every Saturday more new faces appeared, either kids who had somehow heard about our activities or friends of our students who came with them to take classes for a day. A number of them stayed on and joined the school. We evolved an admission policy of sorts by trial and error. As it stands now:

Anyone who wants to spend a day or two taking classes with us is free to do so, to consider whether to join the School.

Kids who don't consider themselves "patients" are welcome to join as well as those who have been referred by psychiatrists or clinics.

Both boys and girls, from midteens to midtwenties are accepted.

Everyone who joins commits himself to at a least a month of regular group therapy and takes whichever classes he wishes.

Any student can change his program when he wishes.

Fees are worked out on a "sliding scale" by discussion with the student and his parents if they are involved.

Fees range from nearly zero to eighty dollars a week. This includes group therapy and all classes.

No one has been refused admission because of inability to pay.

We try to get even the poorest student to make some meaningful contribution, either a few dollars a week or some work to help our staff.

So far, this financial policy has been ethically and morally satisfying to me and to everyone at the School, but it has kept us nearly penniless. We have always been barely able to meet our payroll and pay our expenses. Lately we have been getting a little money from the state of Massachusetts (drug rehabilitation funds). We are seeking morey money to expand our facilities and our program. We do *not* plan to grow in size. It has been clear to us that our success so far depends upon *intimacy*. I feel, and the students and staff agree, that it's important for everybody in the School to know everybody else—and in the greatest depth possible. So we will not grow larger than sixty students. Of course this means that like any private school, we need ongoing help from some source of funds other than tuition fees from kids and parents.

When a new student joins our School, we have a short discussion with him about our program, about the commitment to come to group therapy weekly for at least a month, and we work out a fee. The student signs a simple form to indicate his agreement with these basic conditions. If he is a minor or if his parents will be financially involved, the parents also sign. We got along for two years without any such forms, but occasional misunderstanding with parents arose. After all, some fathers get concerned when their kids commit themselves to what one parent called "some aberrant kind of psychiatric involvement," without consulting their parents about it. And communications are often so poor between kids and parents that parents might not otherwise find out what is going on before a first tuition bill arrives. Hence the forms.

About half our kids arrive either needing individual therapy or already involved in it. In these cases I accumulate whatever medical and psychiatric reports are available. But I do not tell our staff about the particular history of any student unless some issue arises whereby a teacher needs to know more about the student's life in order to deal better with him. I feel this policy avoids labeling the student as "sick," and setting up preconceived notions about him or her in the minds of the staff. This has turned out to be wise, the staff and I agree, partly because most psychiatric "observations" and "evaluations" are conducted under conditions where the patient is at an extreme disadvantage. He may have been in a hospital he did not want to enter, or he may have been forced to consult a psychiatrist by a juvenile court or by his parents with whom he may have been at war. Often an adolescent's behavior under those enforced conditions does not resemble in any way his behavior at our School, where he is free to do largely what he wishes. Very recently a social worker told me of his experience with two adolescent therapy groups. He leads one group at a regional mental health center which is administered in an orthodox fashion—kids come because parents or courts or hospitals send them there for evaluation and treatment. He leads his other group at a local drop-in center, where kids come because they feel like it. He has endless attendance problems with his first group, and he cannot even get permission from his supervisors to call up an adolescent who has quit coming to his group. The policy is that the *parents'* social worker must do that, and then the *parents* must ask the kid to attend. He cannot in that setting even make a home visit, when he is worried about the progress of a kid. In the second setting, the kids want to come, like to come, and only three times in twelve weeks has one kid failed to attend. Much more than adults, adolescents are deeply responsive to the social climate in which they find themselves, and when in an honest and loving environment they seem almost to be different people than elsewhere. Though a third of our kids are high school and college dropouts and many more skip all the classes they can at their regular academic schools, every time a day ends at our School, I have to urge them to go home. They like to be with us, and they don't want to leave.

When a problem arises in the relationship between a teacher and a student, our policy is to:

Brief the teacher on the special information I may have about a student to help him see the student in a new way and to give him suggestions about how to get closer to the student. Sometimes this works in reverse, and the teacher helps me by telling me how he has worked with the student. He may well have found a style that is superior to mine.

These policies tend to allow our students to keep control over how much we are allowed to find out about them, and when. This makes frightened new students feel more secure. One almost mute fifteen-year-old girl (described as "paranoid" by her psychiatrist) attended every weekly group therapy meeting for five months with us, and spoke not a word. She came to art classes where she worked alone apart from the others. Many times members of the group invited Jeannie to speak, to describe how she felt, but she was always silent. At the same time she followed what was happening; you could see that she was absorbed in the group process.

After five months of silence, one night Jeannie found herself at a School party. The party was set up as a series of experiences. You entered a downstairs door to our studio building and found yourself in a small space walled in from other spaces by large flags hanging from the ceiling. In this first room you sat by a fire and warmed yourself. Then you moved on to the next space, where you could have your face painted. Then a room where you got a backrub, then yoga breathing exercises. Then you climbed a ladder up into a small space where people sat in a circle and passed a candle from hand to hand. When you got the candle you were to tell how you were feeling. As the candle went around the circle towards Jeannie, I could feel the tension rise. When she received it, Jeannie looked at the wavering flame a long time, then said loud and clear: "I am getting less scared of people—I'm hoping I'll get even less scared than I am now!"

Letting the patient decide when and how to let us know who he is is a principle long known in psychotherapy and psychoanalysis, but often violated in psychiatric work with children and adolescents. It is always violated in cases of hospitalization and juvenile court involvement, where information about the patient or "offender" is collected by authorities and decisions affecting his future freedom are made over his head. The patient has only one choice: to go along or to resist. At the School, we don't label anyone as a "patient" in the first place; we show our students from the start that their privacy will be respected. We have seen this method earn their trust. Without this trust, nothing would be accomplished, however much information we might have about them.

We started with the arts for several reasons. In the first place, my wife and I, codirectors of the School, are artists. Lois is a dancer, and I am a musician and a sculptor. It was natural for us to see how, in dance or singing or sculpture, you can learn how to improvise, to let yourself go. In an atmosphere like the one Maslow describes, in which no one is comparing you, judging you, competing with you, you reach a point in your art where you go into orbit: you go through a peak experience while creating something new. Then you are left both with the experience, the process of a new kind of being, and also a product—a piece of work that represents you and where and what you are right now. Also, both Lois and I (and most other people we trust) have ourselves been subjected to a series of bad schools where "academic" became associated with boredom, tedium, rigidity, and emotionally dead older people. For us, "art" meant a kind of mystery and freedom. As Dick, our painting teacher, said:

"School for me was such a down trip. Every day it seemed that whatever good and excitement was possible had been canceled for the day, every day. I found my way by going to museums—that's what turned me on, then the High School of Music and Art in New York. Those places saved me."

After we found out that our School was working, we did not limit our curriculum to the arts. We added a number of crafts—leatherwork, silversmithing, weaving, macramé, batik, sewing, and so on. Later, we introduced some academic courses: French, Spanish, German languages and literature and a science seminar. And we discovered that when taught by people who can relate openly to kids, these subjects too turned them on. During this time, we increased our offerings in the arts to include photography, film-making, instruction in woodwinds, piano, guitar, and drums, and blues singing.

Although we are drawn to the possibilities of a full-time school with academics, crafts, and arts combined, we are not eager to become involved with the ridiculous morass of state educational requirements. In order to become an "accredited" school, one must guarantee so many hours of English, social studies, so many school days a year, and so many doors and bathrooms in every building. None of us want to become involved with that system from which we are all refugees. Lately, however, a possibility has arisen of getting some land and building a school on it. In our own atmosphere, on our own terms, we could grow into a full-time school with living quarters for some of the students and teachers. Students who must now divide their days between home, high school, and the School We Have, could then step into a total environment, a twenty-four-hour alternative to the education now available. We are in the process of making this decision.

As of now we are not a residential school. Students decide which classes they want to take, attend them, and go home. Everyone, teachers and students alike, comes to the weekly three-hour group therapy sessions, where the basic rules are exactly what you would expect in any group therapy. Everyone is expected to reveal what he really feels, and we are all equals: teachers are expected to share feelings along with the students.

Until we were forced to leave our original school in the woods, we had a party about once a month. There was food and drink, lots of music both live and recorded, and dancing. Like every other part of the program, the parties were very informal, noisy, and fun. More and more, the kids themselves set up the parties, made the music, cleaned up afterward.

They accepted responsibility because here they were not only allowed to be themselves, they were loved for being themselves. When we find our own quarters once again, there will be more parties.

What is unique is the atmosphere of the whole program. It is a "grooving school," as one boy put it. He is right. And when I spend an hour playing a conga drum in a jam session with our music students and see around me kids loving to play piano and guitar and bass and flute, I feel that the lessons I learned in my own life from attending the *wrong* kind of schools were not in vain. It is not only possible to learn through love; it is necessary. So last Saturday afternoon embracing the conga drum, I looked around at the young faces, smiling and playing together. The question entered my head: "What is this medium?" And the answer followed, "The medium is caring." And the medium *is* the message.

Very early in our group meetings, we evolved a set of policies which help us work and learn together. I laid down two prohibitions, the only ones I have had to make. They are:

Shep's Rule No. 1: *Nobody may bring illegal drugs to our place.* The reason for this is that some of the students have had trouble with the law over drug use, and we don't want our whole program to be closed to *everybody* because some individuals wanted to bring drugs like marijuana or LSD to the School.

In the session in which I announced this rule, nobody disagreed. I made it clear that I consider drug use to be a matter of *personal* policy for everyone. Almost all our kids have used marijuana when they could get it, over half have used LSD and mescaline, and many also "speed" and heroin. We have spent many hours in our group sessions and in individual therapy discussing the pros and cons of psychedelic and other drugs, and I have made sure that our kids found out what these drugs can do to your mind and body. But this first rule simply covers the legal fact that at this time in Massachusetts if you are found to possess illegal drugs, not only do you get arrested, but anyone on the premises with you may be arrested too.

Shep's Rule No. 2: *Don't come to class if you are under the influence of a drug.* The reason I gave for this rule was that we are seeking better communication in a *work* situation. The teacher wants you to understand what the creative task is, in some classes a group task, like a group dramatic improvisation or movement problem. In aikido class, where you throw each other down, your perception, reflexes, and speed must be good or you get hurt. My point was that when you are working with other people, being "high" on any drug makes two-way communication difficult or impossible.

On this rule, there was lots of disagreement. Patty revealed dramatically that she had been "tripping" on LSD that afternoon during dance and drama class, "And I don't think anybody could tell I was doing it. In fact I got really deep into the improvisation [a skit with two other students]. I could really feel things better!" The others in the skit then told Patty (to her great surprise) that they felt they could not get close to her in that day's class. They were bothered by her loud and inappropriate laughter, which kept interrupting the interplay of feelings. Patty was really surprised that they had picked up on her state of mind, which she thought she had successfully concealed. At this point both the dance and drama teachers commented that they too had noticed how Patty had seemed "out of it" in class, how she had slowed up things and disrupted the subtle flow of emotional message and reaction necessary for dramatic improvisation. Patty was chastened. This problem has not arisen with her again.

When the drug problem came up again a few months later, I decided to use the same technique of full group discussion. Two boys had taken LSD one afternoon in the company of another boy. When I was told what was going on, I found them and reminded them forcefully what it could mean for all of us to be caught with LSD at the school. I asked them to leave for the day and return for the next group session, where we would discuss the situation. I also told them I would not let any student endanger our program by inviting arrest and getting us closed up, so that if they did this again, I would not let them return to classes. We would continue therapy outside of the School, but the group activity and our community would not be destroyed because of any student's selfishness.

In the next two group therapy sessions, the whole subject was discussed in depth. All three boys made apologies to the group. From this encounter, one sixteen-year-old boy in particular found out a great deal more about how his own behavior affects the group. Terry heard directly from the other kids how he often claims to do things "for no reason," sometimes getting himself in trouble at school and with his parents and now with our group. Since we like him and since he loves our program, the group wondered why he risks what is so important to him. "Terry," one student asked, "are you *trying* to mess yourself up?" This got Terry thinking. He told us he feels guilty about disappointing his parents' expectations of him. They are very conventional people, and when he gets a poor mark in school or when he was arrested for giving a few dexedrine pills to a girl he knew, his mother weeps and says: "Where did we go wrong? How could you do this to us? Haven't we been good to you and given you everything?" Terry told us this made him feel rotten and deserving of punishment, following which he would do something to get himself punished. This group session was the closest to self-awareness that Terry had yet come. Afterward I talked to his parents and tried to get them to see that it hurts Terry when he gets in trouble and that arousing guilt in him was not only not helping him, but perpetuating the parent-child battle over the issue of *whose* goals will Terry live for, his parents' or his own. Terry has since renounced LSD.

For all three boys involved, the LSD incident resulted in a deeper look at themselves. For this reason, I feel strongly that the use of the weekly group therapy session to discuss what

*What We Do at the School*

goes on in our School is not only justified but essential. Some of the kids still feel that being high on a drug does not interfere with group creative work, but they seem to follow our rule anyway out of respect for the program and what we are trying to do together.

I made no other rules of my own. But soon after we got started, the entire group made a few interesting rules:

Group Rule No. 1: *No matter which classes you are attending, you can try any of the others.* This is subject to the teacher's agreement that there is room for you. Since no class has more than twelve students, class-hopping has never been refused, except in one instance. As the yoga-meditation leader, I had set up a twelve-week session of my class. I accepted as many students as space in the classroom would allow and asked the students to commit themselves to the twelve sessions. Admitting beginners in midsession means the rest of the class must wait while the teacher acquaints the newcomers with elementary yoga postures and techniques. This I felt was unfair to the advanced students. Also, in meditation, students feel more relaxed and secure in letting themselves go when they know everyone in the class. So we don't admit anyone new until our twelve sessions are ended. Then we start a new series and admit everyone who wants to come.

There is a real benefit from letting anybody try any classes he wants. Many times, somebody gets a look at an activity that fascinates him. He may become friendly with people in that class. He would like to join them. Under this group rule, he just shows up and takes the class. Sometimes this brings out new talents or brings to light important problems. Looking back over the results of this policy, I think our students were very wise to arrange things this way. The policy says, "You *can* do things, you *can* learn. There is no limit to what you can try. Don't settle for the narrow view you now have of your talents and potentialities. Look inside yourself and find more promise there than you ever dreamed."

Group Rule No. 2: *You don't have to come to class, and*

*if you feel unable to function in a class, no teacher will press you.* This is an interesting rule. As Maslow pointed out, there are two sets of forces in each of us, one driving us forward toward realizing our potential, toward self-actualization, and another keeping us close to our old sources of security. I think the first student policy, "go to any class you wish," expresses the self-actualization drive of our students. They really want to express and develop themselves as much as they can. The second policy seems to me to express our students' fear of being cut off from security, of being caught in unfamiliar territory without a path of retreat. It is interesting that those who fought for this rule were the most "neurotic" members of our group. That is, their lives had been long on emotional trauma and short on security. They have suffered from a shortage of love and emotional support. These kids wanted something safe to go back to. One boy, John, fought very hard for this policy. He said, "People are always telling you what to do. My parents sent me away to school to become an educated successful person. They didn't accept me as I really am. I could never get love and understanding from my parents when I was scared or hurt. 'Get out there and do what is expected of you' was the message. I don't want to be forced to do anything." If you don't feel up to dramatic improvisation or painting a picture today, if you are depressed or anxious, you don't have to perform in spite of it. Just come to class and work when you are able, and no one will reject you. You still belong.

In fact, almost everyone attends and almost everyone works, but they know they don't *have* to do it—it is up to them. And the teachers know they need not press someone further than he feels safe to go. When the policy is set up this way, no teacher need feel concerned about *how much progress* any student makes. He progresses as fast as he can or as he wishes. No curriculum or rate of progress is defined. Everybody does what he feels ready to do. He uses the teacher, but *he educates himself.* This helps him find out who and what he is, not in the terms of some school system ("under-achiever," "not living up to his potential," etc.) but *in his own terms*.

Group Rule No. 3: *If there is anything we want to learn, and the right teacher can be found, we want to learn it here.* This policy has resulted in our finding some first-rate teachers and developing some fascinating courses at various times, including astrology, rock guitar, welded sculpture, and jewelry-making. In one instance a student named Don developed a passion for blues guitar. He came to me one day saying, "There's only one guy on earth I know who plays better blues piano than I can. I want to study with him. Will you hire him to teach me?" That is how Dave came to teach piano for us. When an adolescent admires someone, it is often for reasons that go very deep. In selecting Dave to teach him, this young man had found someone he wanted to be like, someone he felt he *could* be like. He not only wanted to learn blues style, he wanted an apprenticeship in the life style of a musician. He needed to know how to make a life out of playing blues piano. This student knew *what* he wanted to do; he needed a guide in how to do it. As it turns out, the relationship has been extremely fruitful. Don chose his teacher with the unerring accuracy of the unconscious. His teacher has faced and overcome many of the same problems Don now faces. Don senses this in Dave. He is studying with him on many different levels, and he has become stronger as a man as well as better as a blues player since they have been working together.

Don also got us to set up our astrology class, where he became adept in drawing up horoscope charts. The astrology teacher was helpful to him by showing him a new way of looking at his life goals and those of his parents. The policy of the student selecting his own program of study is followed to a certain extent in college, less often in high school. But in a small program like ours he can even select his own teachers. Lois and I, as codirectors, have final say on selection of teachers. If a student wanted us to employ someone who, in our opinion, was not a good person to identify with or inadequate as a teacher, I would take this up with the student alone or in the group, and we would work out the issue. But so far all the teachers suggested by students have been just right for them. Trusting the students has paid off.

A General Policy: *Problems arising in classes are discussed by the group.* Only a few weeks after the School began this policy resulted in the dismissal of a teacher. The students brought up their dissatisfaction:

**Students:** "He doesn't really show us anything we don't already know."
**Myself:** "Have you told him that?"
**Students:** "Yes, and he just argues that he really knows what to teach us, and if we were *really* hip, we'd agree with him."
**Myself:** "Do you like him as a person?"
**Students:** "No, he's always trying to impress us with how turned on he is! He puts us down."
**Myself:** "Do you think he can change?"
**Students:** "No!"
**Myself:** "I guess I should stop his class, then. Okay?"
**Students:** "But that will hurt his feelings."
**Myself:** "Then should I keep him coming? Will you stay in his class?"
**Students:** "No."

The teacher, with whom I had already tried to work out ways to improve his class, was dismissed. But I feel the students were right. And they learned something about responsibility, because they had to share with me the responsibility for dismissing the teacher, whose feelings *were* hurt. More commonly, problems that come up in classes are worked out successfully in the group sessions by all concerned. Teachers and students reveal their joys and dissatisfactions with each other and figure out better ways to work together.

What makes the School We Have so successful as an environment? Why do kids who previously could not accept school and learning become so self-motivated to learn and to grow? And what makes the School We Have successful with kids who start out, so many of them, deeply disturbed, with tremendous problems in the very areas of the personality which we always thought needed to be intact for learning to take place? Many kids who come to us are wounded in their ability to love and trust anyone and feel deeply that they are worthless, that nothing worthwhile can come out of them. How does our environment help them make the leap that enables them to write and dance and sing and play music? It goes back to the combination of two needs, personal security and creativity, and the fact that these needs are dealt with *simultaneously* at the School We Have. Maslow's lines, re-quoted, are:

> Only the one who respects fear and defense can teach; only the one who respects health can do therapy.

At the School We Have we start with human beings who have fought their own fears and personal problems successfully enough to make creative expression the basic theme of their lives: they become our teachers. The self-actualization of the teacher is the prime reason he is hired. How many schools can say this? Then from those possible candidates, we further select those people who are willing to share with the kids the most intimate details of their struggle to remain creatively alive. When you look for people who are highly self-actualized, living by what they most want to do, and who are at the same time willing to share their deepest feelings with a group of mixed-up adolescents, you are down to a tiny minority of possible teachers. That's why we turn down most teacher applicants at our School.

Most schools leave the actual content of the teacher-student relationships up to the teacher, without much scrutiny, except when some problem erupts publicly between them. Here, too, we are different. We encourage all problems between students and teachers to be aired in the group. And we treat these as problems between people, between equals, where no one is assumed to be right in advance. We don't expect or want the teachers to be therapists, though, in time, after months of group therapy experience they become very adept at finding the deeper sources of interpersonal problems. Every therapy group is led by a professional therapist, someone who makes his life around doing therapy, someone highly self-actualized in that sphere. Either I or Dick, our second psychiatrist, or Bob and Ildre, the psychodrama leaders, are in charge of therapy groups, so that teachers can participate as ordinary members of the group and get as much help as any student.

An example of how even the leader can benefit from the group came up last week for me. I was attacked in my group by Alice, a sixteen-year-old girl who has just completed six months of individual therapy with me while also a student at the School. Alice complained that she had put me on a pedestal as "supershrink" while she was trying to cope with her severe fears and self-deprecation problems, but the better she got the more flaws she found in me as a person. While still thinking of me as supershrink, she had come to feel that as director of the School and as a person I was on a giant ego trip, loving the role of the guy who knows all, who can help everybody, and who likes everybody to come to him with all problems, even though he complains that he has too much on his mind and that everyone is expecting too much from him. In particular, Alice pointed out that I had been very offhand with her in some of our recent moments together, as if I hadn't been listening. She felt my attitude was, "I give you my time in therapy sessions, but I don't care to pay attention to you as a person outside of those." Alice's remarks really hurt me. I knew that I had been getting a lot of ego satisfaction out of being supershrink, and the big wheel at the School. I first admitted to the group that this was true. Yet, at the same time, I had also been feeling too burdened by the almost constant bids for my attention when I am around the School. I went on to say that I have trouble telling someone who seems upset and asks for my attention that I just don't feel like paying attention to him right now, that I'm tired or preoccupied about something else, or, hardest of all for me to admit, I simply don't feel always like being available to help anyone solve a problem right now. So I often pretend interest or push myself into being a sympathetic listener when I really want to say, "Tell me about it some other time." But saying such a thing would make me feel guilty, especially because most of the people who ask for my attention are genuinely disturbed people with serious problems. And I also like most of them.

Suddenly I found myself remembering my mother's comments about psychiatrists long ago when she was depressed and I was a boy of twelve. I recalled her intense devotion to her analyst, "the only one who understands," and once again I could feel her telling me how to win her love, to become the psychiatrist-listener who could hear better and understand more than anyone else. More than that, to fail to become such a God-like therapist would mean that I too had failed her, like everyone else. And I didn't want to have that happen. When this sequence flashed through my mind, I became aware of how angry I was at my mother for setting my life up for me that way. What if I wanted to say, "I don't *want* to listen to your troubles all the time?"

I told the group all this. Then I felt relieved and able to accept the group's advice, which was to tell them directly when I didn't feel ready to hear someone's problems. I agreed to do it, and my life at the School has been genuinely easier since. I consider that I have been helped in important ways by the group, just as any group member has. Bob and Ildre and Dick, our other group leaders, agree that they have gone through similar experiences.

This underlines what everyone at the School comes to feel about the group therapy experience: the group is for everyone, that is, it can give everyone something he really needs. What is it? Recognition of who you are, what your problems and assets are, and acceptance because you are yourself. That is a lot to gain, and it makes the School the key experience of the week for a lot of people, teachers as well as students.

There are, therefore, many differences between the School and the usual "therapeutic" environment, just as there are between the School and other "educational" environments. Basically the difference between us and all clinics or private psychotherapy and psychoanalytic situations is that both patient and therapist are totally involved as human beings, not simply in defined roles where the patient produces material and the therapist helps him work on it. In the School the therapist can and does produce material too, his own problems and concerns, his life history, and the group helps him work on it. There are definite roles at the School— teacher, therapist, student—but these roles do not define all areas of the person. A further corroboration of this closeness is that a great many people at the School have become very intimate friends. Lois and I feel our staff meetings are one of the best experiences of our social life. Many of the kids end up living together and helping each other find jobs, and, best of all, being real friends.

To reiterate, the key factors at the School We Have are the careful selection of self-actualized people to be teachers and therapists, the atmosphere of equality and sharing in classes and group therapy sessions; and most of all, the fact that because of these factors, the School becomes an environment where everyone feels he is there as a person and not just as a teacher, therapist, or student. Ask people who go to schools or clinics or mental hospitals every day if they feel that way. If they did, theirs would be a healing and learning environment.

Dick, the young psychiatrist who leads a group at the School, summed it up at a recent staff meeting: "My group has been unbelievably gratifying lately. I have been able to try all kinds of techniques that I never felt safe enough anywhere else to try. And because I have felt free, the group is working out beautifully. We are honest and real and unbelievably close. The School makes me feel accepted and safe enough to trust my intuitions, and I find a lot of them work!"

One of our students, now at college, wrote in a paper about the School something that helps to make clear our approach:

"When I think of The School We Have,—I think mainly of the people, of the therapy groups—a good feeling, a faith that something is happening keeps me going back; but also knowing there is no coercion. The structure is flexible, but there, so one doesn't have to worry about responsibility for it . . . adolescent patients, especially those interested in artistic or creative fields, get to a certain point in therapy, knowing what they want to do but having nowhere to do it. . . . There was a need for people who could teach and give support to an individual's attempts to explore some artistic fields, some possible alternatives to the dead life around them. So, Dr. Ginandes decided that he would supply an alternative, a place that could serve as a stepping stone.

"There are always unresolved issues from an evening; not everyone finds the School to their liking. Nor is there any coercion to participate in the group; people can sit silently for as long as they want, being asked to respond only if an issue being discussed involves them. . . . The other side is that the individual must take responsibility for his or her self, understanding and help coming only in response to something . . . People leave some groups and talk outside with friends; their desire to be there or not from week to week is respected. Others get pissed when someone isn't there who they would like to be, yet the flexibility is very important to the School. There has been increasing desire for more intensity in groups; psychodrama groups request a commitment for the twelve weeks that they run, and Dick wants a closed group too. Shep maintains his group open to late comers during the evening, not wanting to shut anyone out, though recognizing the desire to have a more intimate group. A student at the

School can set his own pace; yet people are there when he wants them.

"Group is a large part of the support, a lot is shared and worked through: helping to decide, revealing warm feelings, anger. No problem is trivial. There is a core of people who are almost always involved and then those each week who get involved with the particular problem. When I think of the group sessions, I think of Dick's intricate weavings, Shep's funny analogies or stories, people every few weeks bringing something up to show they're still around, talk of leaving the School, a sharing of downs at Christmas time, hugging, crying, the nervous smile, dealing with physical pain, parents' restrictiveness, boyfriend/girlfriend troubles, feelings of being stifled creatively, taken advantage of, not wanting to do anything, 'you're just like me,' a happy story, hassles with other schools, 'I feel better now.' "

# 4 › Saturday at the School We Have

9:30 A.M.:

I back my jeep pickup into my garage and start loading it full of the equipment we will all use today at the School We Have: two big amplifiers for electric guitar and bass, microphones and stands for folk and blues singing, an entire drum set plus conga and bongo drums. Also the School's telephone with jackplug, and a huge wooden chest painted silver, holding tools and materials for our silversmithing class. In Cambridge, Tanya is getting ready to teach leathercraft this morning. She is filling her car with leather tools and hides. Elsewhere half a dozen other teachers are putting together the materials and tools for another Saturday at the School. We have to bring in just about everything we need, then take it all home again at the end of each school day, because we share space in a Concord church with a drop-in center for adolescents and a church school as well. The church is kept open day and night and there are several homeless kids who sleep in the church basement because they can't stand to stay at home. Hence when we tried locking our equipment in a metal garden shed we put up in the church basement, we found most of our things missing. No better luck when we used a room elsewhere in the church, even double-locked. We learned that many adolescents in this town are so bored and fed up with their lives and so hungry for something to do that they will break through any combination of doors and locks to get tools or instruments to use. Occasionally a stray heroin addict has wandered in and broken open our storage cupboards to find something to sell so as to buy junk. It's Concord, Massachusetts, the cradle of liberty, and it's an Episcopal church, but there's no security. Even the coke machine the church installed has been battered open for nickles and dimes. But it's the place we have in which to hold our classes and therapy groups, ever since we moved the School off my own property in our lovely wooded neighborhood. We have an entirely portable School now.

On the way down the road towards the church this sunny Saturday morning I hear a honking and Dick's red Volvo pulls up beside me. He's carrying about six students, our silversmith, and his dog Jules. I am relieved. Dick is here on time today. His drawing class will start promptly and maybe end in time for his four or five students to go on to dance class or the rock and blues class or others taking place this afternoon. Also, I can use the manpower in Dick's car to help me haul all this stuff down into the church's basement (liturgically known as the "undercroft") when we get there in five minutes. That's where we hold our classes and that's where the stuff must be delivered.

Today is a typical Saturday at the School We Have. Dick and Jan will hold a painting-drawing class from ten till one thirty. Because the atmosphere of concrete floors and sliding vinyl folding-panel walls in the echoing undercroft gets them down, lately they've been transporting their art students to Jan's house where she uses her own painting studio. In nice weather they paint outdoors overlooking the Sudbury River and Thoreau's Fairhaven Bay. I have mixed feelings about this—good because the kids swim, eat lunch out of Jan's refrigerator, enjoy the beautiful weather, wander in the woods as well as paint; bad because the class usually starts late and then the kids like to stay at Jan's and thus miss other classes

*Saturday at the School We Have*

that other teachers have planned for them. So the art class at Jan's is high on enjoyment but doesn't fit into Saturday very well. One of our goals at the School is to help the kids find out that whatever they want to do requires some discipline. If there's an attractive woodland picnic going on, it's hard to get them into some other learning experience going on in a less attractive environment.

Dick is a graduate of the Boston Museum of Fine Arts School and an excellent painter. He has been with us since the School started and for a long time he has been a central spirit at the School. He is in his late thirties, black, with a bit of American Indian. He is wiry and muscular and incredibly enthusiastic when he is up. He can sense the feeling of any environment, change it, turn it on. He is a kind of environment magician, and over the past three years he's found for us a good many other unique spirits who have become teachers at the School. His contribution to the *feeling* of the School has been enormous. Dick can make things happen and kids want to be where things are happening.

9:45 A.M.:

When I arrive at the church I enlist Dick's passengers to carry the equipment downstairs and I find my way into the messy little room we call the "School office." Magdyn has just arrived, on time as always. She is carrying in her alligator attaché case the *real* office of the School. It's the same story with the office desk—broken locks and rifled drawers—so all the supplies, stationery, first aid kit, Tampax, God knows what, arrive with Magdyn and leave with her. With a sense of ceremony I plug in the telephone I brought with me, and the School is in contact with the outside world. Half the calls this morning will be from kids looking for other kids, a few from parents looking for their kids who may not have come home last night but would never miss a School Saturday, and some from girls wanting to talk to Dick. Magdyn will answer all these calls and talk to whomever comes around to find out about the School. Some new kids will come to look us over to find out if they feel like joining, some parents will come to see what kind of School their kids are thinking of joining, and so on. Magdyn is in her forties, very trim, in sweater and slacks. She manages our office and she's the only one who knows how we are doing financially. But she is also an astrologer and probably always knows how we *will* be doing financially. Just as well, as I never know. She has been a yoga teacher too, and if there is such a thing as clairvoyance, Magdyn is gifted with it. She pours an enormous part of her energy into the School. She is our only full-time staff member. She is in this "office" whenever the School is in session, and she spends lots of time talking to the various kids who come in to sit on the broken-down couch the church has parked there and tell her what is going on in their lives. She probably knows more of the ongoing events in the lives of the whole School population than any of the rest of us. If you want to know where somebody lives or where they went or when they're due to show up ask Magdyn.

When you know that in the usual high school and many prep schools there is *nobody* on the faculty who knows what's going on in any student's personal life, you come to appreciate this kind of organic involvement that our staff members feel for the kids' lives. The involvement of our entire staff in group therapy, with the kids in the same groups as equals, makes this happen. As time goes by, teachers and kids become friends, important in each others' lives. This is not some kind of a Miss Frances pose, not a front; it is real. Teachers and students regularly visit each other at home, help each other find jobs and schools, meet each other's families, help each other out. The School becomes everybody's extended family: it gives everybody someone to talk to, to ask for help, to share important feelings with. Over time, people in the School tend to become very close.

Magdyn and I go over to the aforementioned broken-down couch, where a very large teen-age boy is sleeping. He is one of the overnight campers in the church basement; not a member of the School but familiar to us. We find him here sleeping almost every week. Gently we wake him up. Then I go out into the undercroft to look for the student with whom I have an interview scheduled at ten.

Marcia is setting up her craft class. She is in her thirties, with long blonde hair, a small intense woman. She is always wearing some fascinating piece of macramé or jewelry she made herself, usually big and in bright colors. Today it is a necklace which looks as if it's made of woven twine, feathers, beads with metal bindings imbedded in it. I have to examine it closely. Lately I'm hoping she will make one of these things for me. Marcia teaches just about every craft you can think of—macramé, crochet, weaving, batik, and tie-dyeing. She could also teach painting and drawing and almost any kind of print-making, if we asked her to. But the reason she doesn't teach these reflects one of the main policies of the School. As much as possible, we want our teachers to teach those skills they have not only been well-trained to do, but those that are basic to their day-to-day identities. Dick not only paints; he is a *painter*. Jan, who teaches with him, is also a *painter*. Marcia in her present phase of creative life is involved with mixed media. Thus she teaches what she is really doing *now* in her life. This fits in with our basic philosophy, with the kind of teacher-student interaction we want at the School. The kids are able to see what the teacher *is*, not just hear what he *says*. To know what the teacher *is* in two ways—in his creative life, the skill by which he makes his life; and in his feelings, which he talks about openly in the group therapy sessions he shares with his students. We don't hire hobbyists for this reason, and mostly we don't use volunteers. Not because they can't be good at their skills and teach very well, but because we are dealing here with *identification* as well as learning, and the kids have to know what the teacher is, loud and clear. How many times have I heard adolescents say about their high school teachers, "My English teacher [or art teacher, etc.] is pretty good, but it's just a job to him. I mean he teaches for the money. At the end of the day he walks out and we don't know each other." This is the kind of observation nobody makes about our School. Many of our kids are dropouts from high school or college or prep school, but it's hard to get them to go home from *our* School. The involvements are real here. Marcia, an art school graduate, is first-rate at what she does. She teaches all day long, taking all comers. By five today the whole area around Marcia will be hung with batiks, tie-dyed shirts, hangings, pieces of weaving that have been worked on today.

10:15 A.M.:

As I search for my first scheduled patient of this morning, Tom and Anne come up to me, hand in hand as always. They are an inseparable couple. About nineteen years old, they have been living together since Tom came out of the hospital, where he was committed when he became psychotic last year. Tom had been a very held-in angry boy in college, fussy about his appearance and conducting an all-out war with two very conservative parents. He came to me the first time as a private patient, largely to get a report from me which would prove to his parents that he was not "crazy like they believe I am." I told him that he was not crazy but full of anger at his parents and spending most of his energy in battling them on unimportant issues. If he got some therapy, I said, he might understand the causes of his anger, get rid of it, and move on to make some kind of life around his own talents and interests rather than remain a guerilla fighter on the home front. Tom refused. Some months later he had a serious psychotic breakdown. He came to the School after four months in the hospital, during which time he had become less psychotic but had completely changed in character. Now he was sloppy in his dress, had long hair and full beard, and seemed not in the least angry. He had become deeply dependent on Anne, moved in with her; Anne loves him too. Together they joined the School. Tom refused my recommendation of individual therapy. After his psychotic episode, Tom has been freer as a student actor, dancer, and guitarist. Anne shadows him, always in sight wherever he is. Intelligent and sensitive in her own right, she avoids the limelight, which Tom usually seeks.

Tom wants to talk to me with Anne about some problems in their love life. I set up a time later when I'm free.


10:30 A.M.:

It begins to look like Herb, my ten o'clock patient, will not be showing up. A sixteen-year-old boy who is almost paralyzed by passivity and depression, he has trouble getting up in the morning. When his parents remind him of his appointment with me, it makes him sleepier and more paralyzed. When I see him Wednesday before our group therapy session, I'd better talk to him about it, since it's the third session out of six that he's missed. We'll probably have to shift the time till later in the day. If we make it at one, just before photography class, he'll make it. He likes photography class and he's getting really good at it. Make a note of that. Now to my surprise, I see Angie walking toward me. A very disturbed seventeen-year-old girl, she left us a month ago to go home to Ohio with her parents, then to return to this area for college. She said she was not going to come back to the School anymore, but here she is, looking for me. As I walk up to her, Magdyn and Marcia also see her; both make sounds of interest and delight to see Angie again, but Angie cuts them both dead as if they were not there. She walks between them, her eyes fixed on me, her face frozen. She radiates feelings of anguish. When I greet her, she seems unable to answer, but looks at me as if about to cry. I take her hand, lead her into a corner where we are less observed. After awhile, she says quietly that she wants to talk to me. Have I got my appointment book? Let's talk now, I say. We walk off to the little room I use as an office. As we walk, I'm remembering the last times I saw Angie. I had talked to her alone a couple of times and had talked to her mother once at length. It's my policy to have at least one session alone with every new student who seems disturbed and one interview with the parents. Angie's mother seemed to be one of those emotionally frozen people who adopt a rigidly structured facade to ward off a psychotic collapse. She had brought a long list of questions and comments about Angie, and could not deviate from it in any way. Not one feeling, not one comment that was not preplanned. Angie later told me that her mother anticipates all her conversations and writes them out before she meets anyone. I found out from Angie that her mother has been this way as long as she can remember. Angie's father is a very busy and successful business executive who buries himself in his work. He *tells* his wife and children what to do and never discusses anything with them. So it was no surprise to me when I had my first interview with Angie last spring that she was a deeply disturbed girl. She had come to the School, as she said, "to find out some way to meet people, to get some friends, to not be so lonely and scared of everyone. There *has* to be a way." Confronted in group therapy sessions by others at the School who told her that they were trying to get close to her but that she was warding them off, Angie didn't at first know what they meant. "You don't answer when we greet you, you don't tell us about yourself. Why don't you, Angie, we'd listen to you!" Angie was starting to loosen up a little when summer came. She came to my yoga class the last two sessions before my vacation. After the first class she came up to me absolutely furious and in despair. "That meditation we do at the end of the class—do the others really get outside themselves? Can they relax and let their minds wander and experience something besides fear? Well, *I* can't! You've got to show me what's wrong!" She felt cheated that she had followed my simple relaxation instructions and had been unable to relax, unable to forget her fear of the other people in the room, of losing control of herself, of everything. I told her that when people are having internal problems they often can't meditate or even relax, especially the first time. "Come next week, Angie, and we'll try again. In the meantime, practice relaxing." Next week Angie returned, and I slanted my instructions to the inert yoga students, all lying on their backs at the end of the class, to suit Angie's problem. I instructed them quietly to let anxieties go, and if fears came, to let them come but not to dwell upon them. I had no idea whether Angie was helped by this, until at the end of the class when she rushed up to me and hugged me. It had worked. I felt this was an important moment for Angie; it *could* be done, she *could* change. But then Angie had thrown herself too far upon the goodwill of the group, asking the next Wednesday night during group therapy for someone who could give her a place to stay for a month; she had nowhere to stay, no money, no friends, and she didn't want to go back to Ohio with her parents. It was too soon; nobody knew her well enough, nobody felt at home yet with her, nobody offered her a place. It was too much to ask. And she was crushed.

In my little office, an empty Sunday-school classroom, the blackboard announces the correct spelling of "Epiphany—Trinity—Ecumenical—Liturgy." Angie sits down on one steel folding chair, I sit on the other. Slowly she starts off telling me how furious she is with all of us at the School for not finding a way to keep her with us for the summer, for not finding a way into her spirit. Her anger pours over. After awhile it seems spent. Now she asks me how she should try to make this closeness happen at college. She's going there tomorrow, she needs to know how to do it—*now*. I advise her to find a professional there to give her some psychotherapy, someone she can rely on and come to trust. I know that it's doubtful someone really first-rate can be found at that college or at most colleges. Yet there's got to be someone who'll recognize Angie's emptiness, her starving baby soul inside the walled-off close face. If there's a therapist there, I can talk to him, I can let him know what we at the School know about Angie. If he's sensitive, if he has time, if Angie goes to see him . . . Angie refuses. "I need *friends*, not therapy!" I point out she needs to learn how to *make* friends, that she doesn't know how yet. Through therapy she could find out why she locks people out, can't let them in. "But why do I do that? Why me?" I go back to what she told me about her mother and father and her lifelong loneliness and feelings of being emotionally starved, her grudge against parents now applied to all people who don't or can't meet her huge needs. All this time I'm aware we have just this one hour to talk. She leaves tomorrow, her college is far away. She needs so much yet makes it so hard to give her anything. I try to get her to agree to try to find a therapist. No. I try to get her to agree to come back and see me on a weekend or vacation—soon. Maybe. Angie is not committing herself. I have no more time now. We part. Have I accomplished anything? I'm worrying about her, and I'm going to worry for a long time. I was so moved by her momentary openness after yoga class that time. Now the walls are up again.

11 A.M.:

I see the silversmithing class is in full swing with five students making earrings, bracelets, necklaces. And in another place the leather class now includes about eight people. The atmosphere is full of busy sounds. In a corner a couple of kids are playing guitars and singing softly. At the other end of the huge undercroft someone has a record player going with loud soul music. The kids like this atmosphere of noise and music.

It fills the otherwise empty space, makes the place cosier. A few stray visiting kids wander from one activity to another, usually to rest someplace and begin to make something. Our students can bring a friend on Saturdays, if the friend is deciding whether to come to our School. Whether or not the friend enrolls, he can make something for himself— leather or silver or batik. This costs us money for materials and tools and the teachers' attention, but I'd rather have that than quiz everyone who wants to do something and refuse to let visitors who may become new students do anything. Part of the feeling of the School is its openness, the trusting atmosphere. Too many enrollment forms, visiting rules, regulations, refusals to let you do this or that would change the atmosphere and make it too much like the schools the kids have come to hate and many have dropped out of.

Now a new girl runs up to me. Long auburn hair, gold-rimmed granny glasses, leotard and jeans, big brown eyes. "I'm Sally. Is it time for me to see you yet?" It is. Sally is new, visiting for the first time, contemplating joining the School. She walks beside me back into the little room in which I just talked to Angie. On the way at least five people accost me with questions and bits of news. Several times I promise to see these people later. Then Sally and I are alone. The first thing she says is, "Please don't say that I can't come here because I'm on probation!" I reply, "Sally, some of our best people are on probation. That makes no difference to us." Sally is relieved, tells me that she has tried to get into half a dozen programs like free schools and drug rehabilitation centers, only to be told that since she's on probation in the Cambridge court, the court is responsible for her rehabilitation. Many programs don't seem to want her. "What do you want here?" I ask. Sally replies very directly, "Love and peace and something to do." Then she shows me a leather pouch hanging from her belt, also a silver ring, both of which she has already made in about an hour and a half at our School. "It feels good to make something with your own hands. When you start feeling down, you can look at it and remind yourself you can do something pretty well!"

Sally has run away from home three times, once for six weeks. But it's high school she was trying to avoid. It's a jail, she says. "We have this American Civilization teacher. She stands there and tells us how great this country is. I raise my hand to ask, 'How about Viet Nam? How about the blacks? How about the poor?' but she never calls on me."

"You mean she calls on others, not you?"

"No. She says, 'You're all here to learn, so keep quiet and listen and you'll learn.' It's just propaganda."

Sally's misfortune is that she's become a political and social radical too early, at fifteen. Along with her adolescent rebellion against her family, she has outgrown her parents' conservative view of things. Her greatest experience was her runaway to Washington, where she joined with older college kids in weeks of protest against American policy in Southeast Asia. She feels she learned more there than she ever did in high school. When she came home she was put on probation as a runaway and forbidden to run away again or to refuse to obey the "lawful regulations of her parents." But no one in the court has helped her find a broader kind of education, a wider world to live in. So she's in a kind of jail at home now. Sally tells me her father has had nervous breakdowns since he was a soldier and has to go into the VA hospital every once in a while for a few weeks. He's a plumber, doesn't make much money, there are seven kids younger than she is. "But my mother and I get along cool. She does some sketching and drawing, she tries to get me art supplies. But the other kids get jealous."

It's obvious that Sally and our School are made for each other. I accept Sally as a student as of this minute. I'll call her mother and hope she can pay ten dollars a week. Actually it costs us about forty dollars a week per student to run the School. We take kids who can't pay, nonetheless; that's a unanimous decision of staff and students. I'm hoping the state

*Saturday at the School We Have*

will pay under the heading of "delinquency prevention" for some of these kids who don't have resources. One of the programs which refused to admit Sally because she is on probation has received $25,000 from the state this year as a "delinquency prevention program." How does that figure? But then putting a kid on probation for running away doesn't figure either—not without more direct help for the family.

Sally and I talk for awhile longer. I make a mental note that there must be some deeper feelings about the family or else she would not have run away so often for so long. She's not aware, probably, how strongly she feels about something going on at home. I'll need a session with her parents for history and to understand her situation better.

This is a policy, talking to the parents of kids who come to the School with obvious problems. It's often a bit tricky to see the parents of adolescents who have been at odds with them for a long time. The atmosphere between some of these kids and their parents has become so paranoid that seeing the parents seems dangerous to the kids: "You'll probably get on *their* side, like the probation officer, the social worker. . . ." So sometimes I don't see them myself. I ask Mary to see them. Mary, a teacher and counselor on our staff, does quite a bit of work with parents for us, sometimes because of the enmity between kids and parents, sometimes because of her ability to understand what the parents are going through while not losing her allegiance to the kids. Mary has written something recently about how working at the School has changed her as a parent, which I'll quote in the chapter on families.

Or I might see Sally's parents together with Sally. I do that when there are concrete issues to work out between a kid and parents. Since Sally now tells me that her father has refused to sign the paper that says he agrees she may come to the School and that her mother has signed it for her ("Don't tell your father . . ."), it's pretty clear that we'd better get together and talk about how both parents feel about Sally's running away, her style of life, and her coming to the School. If we can't get the least possible scrap of understanding and cooperation from them, their sabotage may wreck Sally's coming to us. We've seen it very often. Even when we waive the payment of our fees by parents and let kids pay what they can when they can—which is why we're always broke—there are so many little ways parents can show kids they are against the kids' involvement with us. No money for bus fare, no permission to come to School, or something else the kid has to do, etc. And determined parents can wear the kid out with these obstructive measures till there's simply no energy left to fight them or till the adolescent, frustrated and angry, does something obvious to call attention to his dilemma. A new overdose of drugs, a suicidal gesture, a runaway. So we'll try to prevent these, talk to Sally's parents soon, try to make some rapport. And we'll get in touch with her probation officer and make sure she knows Sally's coming to us and that she'll encourage the parents to accept the plan. Here my years as a director of court clinics comes in handy. I know how to deal with probation officers because I'm familiar with the difficult circumstances in which they must work. Translating the decision of a judge into a workable plan whereby an adolescent can find some kind of a life for himself despite a very difficult family situation, is a hard job and I sympathize with it. Maybe I can show Sally's probation officer that the School is in Sally's best interests and maybe the probation officer will step in to show Sally's father that the court approves. We'll see.

**NOON:**

As I pass by the silversmithing class, I see five kids still working intently over pieces of jewelry. They're sitting at a big old table that Dick once scrounged for the School. The top is all scarred and pitted, burned here and there by a torch that strayed off the edge of the asbestos sheets we put on top of the table. The silver class is usually quiet and intent. As I pass, Bates gets up and greets me. She is twenty-three, tall and slim, a beautiful young woman in a thirties house-dress she bought in a goodwill store. Today she is wearing a lovely necklace, a chain she made herself. Bates and I have a special good feeling for each other. She has a sweet passivity, a live-and-let-live attitude that works wonderfully with the kids. She too went to the museum school, graduated, and started making her life as a silversmith, selling her work on consignment in various Harvard Square boutiques. When I meet the kind of high school teachers the kids complain about, the ones who *judge* everyone and everyone's performance, I think of Bates. She accepts what people are; that's their trip. Some of the shyest and most frightened kids who come to the School find Bates's class a safe place to start relating to us. Maybe that's why she sits right up near the door where you enter.

Despite some hard times in her personal life, Bates found it hard to use the group at School as a place in which to discharge feelings, work out solutions. But recently when she left her old man, Bates did tell us about it, and got a lot of support from us. She was able to express her feelings that she needed more from life than she was getting. Since then she has been more involved in the group therapy at the School.

The policy we've developed for group therapy is simple: You don't *have* to say a single word in a group at the School. It's quite enough to come and listen to others. But when you do speak, we ask that you say what you really feel. As one kid put it, "Better shut up than bullshit." A number of our kids have spent weeks, even months, coming to group therapy and saying nothing. Bates is almost the only member of our staff who used the group this way. She'd come, listen, say a few words of encouragement about someone else's problem, but rarely bring up her own. Then her own life problems needed discussion, and she had nowhere to go to talk about them. One night she decided to tell us about it. The response of the group was supportive. Listening to Bates meant a lot to a number of our girls. Bates had tried for awhile to subjugate her own needs to those of her man, to minimize her demands. It was an old-style relationship in which she felt *his* needs came first, that she should be what he wanted when he wanted it. She felt taken for granted, used, and began to realize that she wanted a new kind of relationship in which she was an equal. Some of the girls and women in the School are working on the same problem, at fifteen with a boyfriend or at forty with a husband. She found out that staff and students alike were attuned to these issues and we helped her feel stronger about her decision to move out and start over. This session seemed to bring her closer to the group.

Hugging Bates this morning, saying hello, makes me think back to that session and to the fact that for her, as for many of us, the group at School has become in a way like a good family. Most of the people at the School, students and staff alike, have simply no one else they feel as safe to go to when they need to work out some feeling. The kids particularly: most of them feel that if they go to their parents with their deepest personal problems they won't be heard, but judged. My experience with many families tends to make me agree. They would indeed be judged. Sometimes family therapy can change that—making the family into a therapy group, showing everyone how they deal with everyone else. But that's a lot of work and stress, most families won't agree to it. So for many of the kids, it's the group at School where you take your problems. For now, the only parents we work with are the few who come for family therapy with me, or two or three who come to see Mary. Another problem to be thought over in depth and maybe solved.

**12:30 P.M.:**

Today I'm having lunch with Barbara, a social worker who is looking for a job. She called me the other day and I told her we haven't the money to hire any more staff, but she said she didn't care that much about money for the next few months, and she'd heard we were doing interesting work. Also, she has experience as a fund-raiser for youth projects, and that interested me. I find Barbara talking with a couple of kids from the leather class. As I come by, she finished talking with them and we walk off toward my car. Barbara is in her late twenties, wearing jeans and a knitted stole. She is bright, earnest, very open, and direct. As we head for the car, three kids want to know where we're going—can they have rides? Turns out we are all going to a fish place where you can get clams, fish, scallops for lunch and it's pretty cheap. We end up with a carful of riders.

At lunch Barbara tells me her experience with shrinks and some of the "mental health" institutions she's worked for. She feels psychiatrists are among the most inaccessible people she's ever known. "Businessmen, at least they get angry, they can say 'no' if they want to. But shrinks! They are so evasive. They won't tell you if their programs are working, or how well, they won't tell you whether they want to change them, or how; you can't feel you've really encountered them, made real contact." Barbara feels the regional mental health centers and clinics she has worked in are *not* working, especially for young people. I agree. I tell Barbara that this is why after twenty years working in the mental health structure of two states, being clinic director, chief consultant, etc., I've finally quit the system and set up my own place, the School. But now the problem is how to get financial support and community help. The existing mental health bureaucracies have money, lots of it. My twenty years' experience showed me that much of that money is wasted. When you realize that what really counts in mental health work is the honesty and depth of a relationship between the patient and the therapist, you realize how little is accomplished in most mental health institutions. In most clinics and hospitals, too few patients feel they have made real contact with a therapist, much less gotten any real benefit from such contact. You have to make a relationship for therapy to do any good. Except for the situations of acute psychosis where hospitalization keeps the patient from hurting himself or somebody else while he is actually psychotic, and the emptying of the back wards of chronically psychotic patients by the use of thorazine and other tranquilizers, the mental health establishment has not impressed me. The real problems of the people who are going through life crises are generally not met by the available clinics; it's too slow and frustrating to call up, get an appointment for screening by a social worker (late next week), then after that session you are scheduled to meet with a supervising psychiatrist and three residents in training (that's the week after next), then you wait to hear from the clinic as to whether you are accepted for therapy. Then, if you are accepted, perhaps a couple of months later you meet your therapist, and he's a resident still in his training. Even if he helps you, usually at the end of June he is leaving the clinic and you get reassigned to another therapist. And so on. I've known people who went through five therapists this way.

Barbara and I see eye to eye about institutionalized mental health programs. But what can we do for each other? We work out that she wants to become a member of our School, come to therapy group for a few months, learn our style. She'll regard it as part of her training. All I can offer is that if this phase works out to our mutual satisfaction, *if* we get some money from somewhere to enlarge our program, then *maybe* I can offer her a part-time job afterwards, leading a therapy group, which is her experience and her wish. I like her; she has energy, she is intelligent, she doesn't accept things the way they are without trying to change them. She ought to have somewhere to work where she feels at home, where she feels excited and challenged. Last month I hired a young psychiatrist on the same basis. But there's a limit—I don't know how we'll have jobs for these outstanding young therapists, or when. It comes back to finding money for the School. And we're trying to do that now, and I'm not good at it, and I don't like it. Writing proposals for grants, looking for private benefactors, it all takes energy away from what I want to be doing—working with the School directly and creatively. Working with the *people* here, not so much administration!

2:30 P.M.:

I've had my session with Tom and Anne, who are struggling to untangle their symbiosis. They love each other, but they also *need* each other so deeply, and their relationship is so tangled with their deepest insecurities, that they can't seem to make a move without each other. We have agreed on regular sessions as a couple, for awhile, to work on this. I feel good about that decision.

Now I'm sitting in a little dark room at the end of a long basement hallway and through two fire doors. It's called the "jam room" because it's where David runs his rock-blues and jazz jam session every Saturday afternoon. I try to get in for half an hour every week, partly to work on my conga drumming, partly to watch David's expert work with our young musicians, and mostly to enjoy the wonderful sounds David can produce from this mixed bag of talent.

David is very tall, pale, skinny, and black-bearded. He always seems to be standing or sitting a little crooked, leaning over a bit. He looks like an El Greco painting I saw a long time ago, Jesus after going through some hell. And David has a voice that comes from somewhere in the bottom of his chest, a baritone horn from inside this tilted stovepipe. Usually there are a few music students in the jam room stumbling through the dim light setting up amplifiers and practicing riffs, long before David arrives. For an hour before he comes, people are asking each other, "Is he here? Did you see him? You sure he's coming today?" They all know David as a superb performer, absolute master of blues piano; they know that whenever the blues greats come to Boston—John Lee Hooker, Big Mama Thornton, Muddy Waters, they all call up David, get David to play piano with them wherever their gig is. And the kids also know that David is fully trained, and knows exactly what he's doing musically. He has a great ear, but he's not a by-ear musician. He can play the scales, construct the chords, knows harmony and music theory, and he can teach these things to you. So the atmosphere is that the star is due to arrive.

Bill, who plays bass guitar in the jam, is describing having seen David accompanying a dance class at Radcliffe College—this is one of the patchwork of music jobs which add up to David's income. "David managed to put these blues and jazz riffs into exactly the rhythms the teacher was asking for. Yet the added melody line and David's ideas were telling the dancers how to hold their bodies, what the *feeling* of the dance was, as well as giving them the beat. And then in the second half of the class David disappeared and came back with a piece of glass and a quarter, opened up the piano and started scraping the strings inside it. How he managed not only to make those weird sounds, but to keep them in tempo and actually to make a melody line out of it, I don't know. It just made the dancers *move*—turned the class into an exciting event. When the accompaniment is that creative, it inspires the dancers to open up, too—they came alive."

Now David arrives. He is wearing a beat-up straw hat, like the ones the old black blues singers always seem to wear—also a red undershirt and some old black pants. And all the sound of practicing and amp tuning and drum play dies away, and David gets the group together. He fits the talent into some musical structures that the assembled talent can play. So the beginners, the pretty good, and the first-rate musicians soon find themselves playing together, learning ensemble playing. They get gradually bolder and freer, taking the solos David assigns. Sometimes these numbers go on for half an hour or more, like Indian ragas; as they stretch on they get better and better, more together. Feelings start to come out on guitar, piano, horns, bass, blues harp, interspersed with blues verses shouted by David. Then David gives the mike to Jane, who is a fine blues singer. She takes a few choruses with deep feeling, and now the group feels really welded together by the music.

David has made his main contribution to the School this way, as a teacher, from the very beginning. Like Bates, David for a long time did not choose to use the group therapy sessions for bringing forth his own problems anywhere near as much as some other teachers have, though his presence was felt in the group through comments and advice to others who were working out their own problems. The main message David gives is that he devotes his life to the expression of his feelings through music, and that in order to do that job supremely well, he has accumulated ample discipline and formal training. Working with him, the kids find out that training serves the expression of feeling, that you can't express enough musically without the training. The dream of being a famous rock or blues musician, another Mick Jagger, gives way to the reality of how long it takes to get your chops working right, how many hours, days, weeks, months, or practicing you need. David has the gift of making the kids want to learn more, to do it better. As I leave the jam to go to aikido class, I know I'll have to come back around five to remind David that the church people want the jam to end before five thirty (so the janitors can clean up for Sunday festivities). I also know that unless I personally *make* the jam end, David will keep it going for another hour or two because it becomes so exciting, so utterly absorbing, that no one will remember or care what time it is. And I really want them to go on, because the closeness of the shared creative project is what the School is all about, and you can't schedule that to end at some arbitrary hour. But I'm the director and I'm responsible to the church people, so we can't have a marathon jam until we get our own place. In our own quarters, shared with no one outside the School, we'll have jams that continue until it feels right to stop. The clock comes last.

Lately David has entered a new phase in his relationship with us. Last spring he went away to work at a college for four months, and when he came back he found us having serious money troubles. Our music equipment was in bad shape and we couldn't pay him as much to teach anymore. David got angry about it and he has begun to speak up in the Wednesday School meetings about the poor equipment, poor financial situation, and their effects on his morale as a teacher. He finds it harder to make the Saturday magic happen within these limitations, he feels we are not taking good care of him and of the music department. When I heard he felt this way, I wanted him to bring it up at one of our monthly staff meetings. But he had a playing job that night, so I asked Bill to come to the staff meeting and present the case for David and for himself as a student and musician. Bill had been talking all these problems over with David. For a while now he has been very close to David, spending lots of time with him at his own place and David's. They are close friends now, and David's resentment of the situation has stimulated Bill to speak up in his support.

Bill really brought it all out last week at the staff meeting, and went lots further than just the money and equipment problems of the music department. It was as if these had touched off some of his lifelong resentment of authorities and adults who don't hear your feelings and don't help you express yourself. Bill accused the School of being sick—emotionally and financially. He felt the classes weren't working, the groups weren't working, the School was dying. He remembered the days in the old studio at my place, when we were thirty, not sixty people, and when we had one group therapy instead of four every Wednesday night. He felt that the closeness and intimacy of that time was gone and that the closeness of contact and understanding between the School and its teachers and students as individuals was getting lost. This was the tensest moment at any staff meeting since our beginning over three years ago. Various teachers asked Bill for specific examples of when and how classes and groups had failed. Still angry, still sure he was right, Bill couldn't find more examples than the music situation. He explained that he is now a full-time student at a professional music school in Boston, and he wants to find as high a level of professional music training at our School as he finds there. He's not getting it from us.

One by one teachers began telling how they feel about their classes. Several have problems with the space they are in, the equipment they must work with, the problems of taking everything home at night so materials won't be stolen or destroyed in the church between class meetings. But just the same, Marcia felt her craft classes had never been better or more productive. June felt the same about her drama classes, and added that she has been thrilled with the new theater workshop group that she and Lois have started this month. They are working toward a production and the level of dramatic skill and discipline is very high. Lois agreed. Bob and Ildre, our psychodrama group leaders, reacted to Bill's anger itself as well as to the content of his remarks. They felt he was being arrogant, damning the School in an all-inclusive way, expressing some feelings out of his own life as well as realistic facts about the School. They pointed out that Bill had quit their psychodrama group after two sessions without even telling them why he left. In the exchange that followed, lots of things emerged. For one thing, the staff as a whole understands and agrees with some of Bill's criticisms of our financial, equipment, and space problems. We are just as tired as Bill is with the waiting to raise $100,000 to get us some land and a building of our own. Dance classes on concrete floors without a bar or mirrors, art classes without a place to store half-finished work between one class and the next, a drum set Shep has to haul out of his garage every Saturday and then put it back, no place for welding or sculpture, no photographic darkroom, and so on. But then another thing emerged. June and Lois and other teachers described a shift in their ideas about the goals of their classes as they had become familiar with the School. June: "It's not that I'm doing drama *therapy*, but my initial ideas of having a disciplined drama company had to change when I saw how different the kids are. Some are ready to be there on time and work hard, and some can't even keep still while the others are doing an acting improvisation. I had to give up the professional goal, or at least postpone it. After three years, now at last we have a small group who can produce a real piece of theater, and they'll be as good as anyone could be!"

Lois, who has been teaching movement in her shared theater workshop with June, agreed. She pointed out to Bill that we are not starting with strong and motivated preprofessional students like some of those in his professional music school downtown, but with people who, like Bill himself when he started with us, don't know what they can do, don't know in fact if they're strong enough to do *anything*. And a lot of time and energy is spent in *relating* to the students, helping them feel safe with us, secure enough to show us what they can do in any of the disciplines we teach.

What emerged at that staff meeting was a concept that the School We Have is a *preschool* for creative adolescents. What you can accomplish in this preschool is to get to know yourself better as you really are, complete with the feelings you have never yet wanted to look at. That's the therapeutic goal. Then if you want to, you can go on to find out how to become an artist or a musician or a dancer from people who already are. The staff meeting marked Bill's arrival at the point where he decided to become a musician and was angry at anyone who stood in his way.

After the meeting, Bill was shook up. His next therapy session with me was tremendously productive. Because Bill knew that he had been listened to, that his comments had been taken seriously point for point, and that he had not been dismissed as just a student with problems, he had to reconsider his initial idea that the staff of the School weren't interested in who he is or how he feels. He felt all of us caring about him. But he also had become aware of his enormous anger, his readiness to indict us as another gang of adult authorities who have lost touch with what is basic. In this therapy session Bill began to see how his anger at his own parents, who have truly deprived him, had been the fuel for his rage at the School. His therapy has moved much faster and deeper since the staff meeting.

As I think over this incident, I am tremendously proud of the School and our staff. These people had been able to show Bill a kind of sensitive attention that no one could show him before, yet we stood up to him and we didn't let him get away with blanket indictments of the School and its work. In fact, Bill's attack was a valuable moment of reassessment for us.

And the benefits did not stop there. I asked Bill to report to David the results of the staff meeting, because some of his feelings were shared by David; then I set up an appointment to talk to David about his specific problems as a teacher, and to try to work them out. More important, I brought up the subject at the next all-School meeting. I described the staff meeting, Bill discussed his point of view. I asked if the members of the School wanted to know what our financial problems were, why we had a shortage of equipment, why we haven't got our own building; in fact, would they like to hear our entire budget? They would. So we spent an hour and a half on that, and went over who gets paid what and why, how much everything costs—the works. The feeling came out that when most of these kids want to know the financial workings of their family budgets, they don't get answers. They are patronized, not included in the shared concept, "This is the amount of money our family has to work with." Lots of questions were asked. After all were satisfied, we went on to other subjects. Now the students know that they can come to staff meetings when they have quarrels with School policies, that these subjects are to be dealt with openly. And I don't feel quite so lonely as the director. An interesting sidelight of the budget discussion is that within three days, a good many students paid their tuition fees.

#### 4 P.M.:

It is time for aikido class. For me, this is pleasure. After a Saturday of dealing with human problems and administrative decisions, I finish the day as a student. Aikido is one of the Japanese martial arts, the most recent one to be evolved. Our teacher (the Sensei) is a marvelously agile Japanese man who comes out from his own *dojo* in Cambridge to teach at our place. He arrives with a small entourage of his own students who transport him to Concord and take the class with our students. That's good because his students speak English and can explain some things to our students that the Sensei can't tell us in words.

Aikido is a marvelous discipline for people who need to learn how to handle aggression. Both for those, like me, who as children ran away rather than fought back, and those who are too angry and need to control their aggression, aikido provides a discipline which teaches you how to handle being attacked. You emerge in control, your attacker is immobilized, and no one gets hurt. I have been taking this class for two years, since the Sensei came to us. Dick had found him first, arranged for the Sensei to give us a demonstration one afternoon on a large mat out among the pines near the School's old studio. After watching this lithe little man cope with being seized by four 200-pound Black Belts at once, around the neck, arms, and legs, I was impressed. There would be a blur of movement, and all four attackers would end up on the mat, while the Sensei remained there cooly without even seeming to perspire. I envied his alertness, his agility, the feeling that he could cope with anything that came along.

As a teacher he is marvelous. Speaking almost no English, he teaches by example. We warm up first, doing what he does—stretching, bending, loosening various joints. Then we take partners and repeat the throws over and over. When attacked *this* way, you can respond *this* way, or *that* way. Each class we learn three different attack-response combinations. The Sensei teaches us how to deal with a punch, a chop, a knife, a gun. And he senses the problems of each student. When someone is frightened, the Sensei throws him to the mat as gently as you would put a baby to bed. When someone is too rough, the Sensei shows him how that feels on the receiving end. No one has been hurt physically or emotionally in the class. And the Sensei has faced all kinds of human problems from the deeply paranoid to the aggressively delinquent. He can feel what your aggression status is and help you with it. He has made some allowances for our School's flexible style. He lets students come and go, never complains about those who float off in the middle of the class. He leaves the problems of getting the students there, keeping order in our space, entirely to me. I know that in his own *dojo* he is more traditionally authoritarian. He felt this way would work better for us, and it does.

Because I know these kids and some are my patients, I get special pleasure in seeing them work out deep problems through aikido. Randy, who is sixteen and a paranoid schizophrenic, fears that everyone wants to kill him. But he has learned in aikido that he can throw others down and they don't retaliate, that he can let himself be thrown and not suffer injury. It has meant a lot to him to place this reality up against his fantasies of destruction. And Joe, who is very tall and thin, is working out his problem of learning how to defend himself. Always shy and submissive, he backed down when challenged. No one in the family encouraged him to fight back when he was teased or attacked by other boys. He took a lot of punishment and felt like a coward. He doesn't want to hurt anyone, but he doesn't want to be paralyzed with fear if someone threatens him in the city, where he lives alone. So he takes aikido, and in a few months I have felt his body tone change from trembling tenseness to relaxed flexibility as we work out together.

I like what aikido is doing for me physically and also in terms of my own self-image. Brought up by my mother and grandmother who were both panicked by violence, they never encouraged me to defend myself against attacks by bigger kids. And I was puny as a child and slow to develop until I was thirteen. My father wasn't home much either, so I couldn't find any training in what to do when some bigger boy wants to take your lunch money away from you, except to give it to him and hope he won't also hit you. Aikido makes me feel I have a vocabulary of responses to attack and less fear of responding aggressively.

5 P.M.:

The aikido class ends with "stretch back," in which the Sensei takes me on his back, back-to-back, and I get a back stretch, then I do the same for him. We kneel on the mat, bow to each other, and rest a moment. Then we put the mats away, and School's over. I go down the hall, sidle through the musicians in the dim jam room, all playing a funky blues, whisper in David's ear that it's time to quit. He nods without opening his eyes. That means maybe half an hour later the musicians will struggle upstairs to my jeep with amplifier, drums, electric piano, etc. Meanwhile I'll load up the batik stuff, the silversmithing stuff, and by six I'll be home, feeling tired but pleasantly spaced-out. It's an unusual kind of adolescent psychiatry I am doing here, but it beats sitting in an office all day. At the School, we are not simply talking about life, we are living it together.

# 5 › Kids

AT THE BEGINNING, the kids who attended the School were patients. All were in psychotherapy, all needed work on deep personal problems mostly dating from early childhood. Problems of mistrust, despair, self-destructiveness, anxiety, fear of rejection, inability to get into some form of work, to commit themselves, to finish whatever they had started. These symptoms are familiar to any therapist who treats the neuroses, and "character disorders" of young people. But within the very first month, something interesting began to happen. Kids came up the road to find out what we were doing. A friend or a friend's friend turned them on to some kind of school in the woods where people were playing blues, painting, doing dance and drama. Some kids just wouldn't be a part of it. Others were eager to join. "Do you have to be fucked up to come up here?" We let them in if they could agree to stick to it for a couple of months. Some of these kids turned out to have problems requiring intensive therapy, just like the "clinically referred," but most of them turned out to suffer from a cultural disease, that of being a creative adolescent in our society. They came not for therapy, but for *guidance* toward realization of the creative forces within themselves, guidance in creative ways to blend imagination, inner freedom, into some sort of identity. These kids enjoyed the free and spontaneous style of our classes, the beauty of group self-exploration.

As it turned out, the presence of these kids, who are not so much disturbed as they are searching for their best selves, helped the School immeasurably. They are one of the vital ingredients of the therapeutic environment, lending vitality and purpose, commitment, and self-assurance to the atmosphere. They are models for the more disturbed kids, *but* models in the role of peers. There is no separation of any kind between this and that group. No one is labeled; the kids form their own judgments of one another.

Who are the kids who come? Where do they come from, and what do they come for? Let me introduce some of the adolescents who came seeking ways to a better life and thus became founders of a new experiment in relating to older people and to their own insides:

BETSY: "AREN'T THERE ANY WHOLE PEOPLE IN THE WORLD?"

Though she was eighteen, Betsy looked no older than fifteen when she first came to see me. Her long brown hair hung down, covering most of her face. As we talked, I got tiny glimpses of a blue eye or the end of her snub nose or a few freckles. It was four months later after she had begun to feel better about herself that Betsy let me get a look at her features. She was referred to me by her probation officer and a psychologist from the court clinic. Betsy was arrested for living with a boy she was not married to. In Massachusetts the law calls this "lewd and lascivious cohabitation." A neighbor had become incensed at the immorality next door and called the police.

Betsy's parents had been battling for almost twenty years. Betsy's mother is a successful business woman who prides herself on getting things done efficiently, "better than most men, I might add!" At home, she is also the executive director and dominates the life of the family. When I talked to her alone she showed me that quality of frustrated rage that so often marks the woman who makes a cause out of proving and reproving that she is as good as any man. When she later could discuss the failure of the whole family and her imminent divorce, she revealed that her forceful efficiency had been the cover for her own feeling of worthlessness. If she could prove she was *really* the best, maybe someone would love her.

Though Betsy's father is also a successful executive, he is quiet and soft-spoken. He told me that he was always closer to Betsy. "I could see that she wasn't really appreciated by her mother. I tried to make it up to her." Whenever he could, he gave Betsy whatever she wanted, even things her mother had refused her. But always on the sly; when mother was around, he withdrew silently and appeared to bow to her will. When another daughter was born, Betsy found out she could get more attention than the baby by revealing how deprived and angry she felt; she would be naughty, throw temper tantrums, run weeping to her father. When she did this it caused further battles between her parents and this became Betsy's revenge against them.

Partly as a result of battles over Betsy, the parents separated a few times, spoke of divorce which finally occurred. By the time Betsy was fifteen, the combatants had taken rigid positions:

**Mother**: "Betsy is on her father's side, and she secretly hates me. She is writing stories and poems, and showing them to her father to seduce him onto *her side*. They are both working against me. I can't keep Betsy around any more. She has to go!"

**Father**: "My wife has never really loved me; she only wants to dominate me. I don't know why I stick to her—maybe because I am weak. She makes me feel weak and angry inside. But I love the children more than she does, and I want to save Betsy from her. I must give Betsy the love her mother can't give her. If I side with Betsy, I can get even with her mother at the same time."

*Betsy*: "My mother is a drag; she pushes everybody around. She thinks she knows everything but she really knows nothing. She can't even feel pleasure in anything she does. And my father—he tries to make me love him by giving me everything I want, even if it's something I shouldn't have. That makes me feel contempt for him. He's spineless. I've got to get *out* of this house, but why do I end up hanging around with these mixed-up hopeless boys? I look for strength in somebody and wind up taking care of *them!* Aren't there any *whole* people in the world? Isn't there some strong person who would love me because I'm me?"

Betsy was the victim of the neurotic problems of her parents. With a father whose passivity and submissiveness covered his inner anger at his wife, and a mother who needed to dominate her husband and children, family life was constant combat. And this kind of domestic war makes it very difficult for the kids to grow up and mature, since the parents are combatants, and each tries to enlist the sympathies of the kids against the other. If you are a son in such a scene, you may not respect your father's slimy evasiveness, but you also hate being pushed around by your mother, who wears the pants in the family. So you have a hard time deciding who you want to be like.

As the oldest child and a daughter, Betsy needed her mother not only for care, but as someone to identify with. But every interaction with mother was a contest. There was always some way in which Betsy wasn't pleasing her mother and needed to do this or that before she would get her approval. When kids have this kind of dilemma at home, they can sometimes find someone at school, a teacher, guidance counselor, someone with whom they can pick up the threads of development in an adult-child relationship. If this new parent figure is able to give some real attention and caring, then some affection and later identification begins to take place. But in the public schools of Concord, Betsy had found no adult who had the time or energy to get close to her. Most public schools deal with kids in such large numbers that individual relationships depend too much on the child having the energy and perseverance to seek out the adult and to start the relationship off. This never happened for Betsy. Whatever strengths and talents she had were little noticed by anyone, and thus never resonated back to her in the form of adult encouragement and praise. She was nobody at home, nobody at school.

### BRAD: "EVERYONE LIVES ON SOMEONE ELSE'S MISERY."

Brad looks the typical hippie. His long lank yellow hair falls below his thin shoulders. He likes wearing tattered bellbottom jeans patched with bits of the American flag, a cowboy leather vest over an ancient mottled shirt, and suede boots with flapping soles. At sixteen he is small and slight, weighing perhaps a hundred pounds. But his eyes are luminous. When I first saw him, it seemed his whole body was a skinny scaffold built to support those huge blue eyes which were full of such feeling. Mostly I saw pain and despair but at times when Brad felt more secure and successful, his eyes would fill with humor and creative excitement.

Brad had been committed to a large state mental hospital for over a year, emerging with the schizophrenic label. He was committed there after a long year of disappearance from home and wild indulgence in every kind of drug he could get hold of. The list included pot, hashish, LSD, mescaline, speed, and finally heroin. He found the psychedelic drugs like LSD and mescaline opened up too many painful fears and hallucinations of murder, but the "downs" like heroin gave him short periods of comfort and ease, a feeling he never found without drugs. When he got out of the hospital, the doctors felt he could not make it in regular high school. The local school authorities were just as happy about this. Brad's long hair, hippie clothes, and his history of drug use made them fear that he would bring drugs into the school if he were admitted. Brad accepted this decision, since he had always found school a bore. "No one there ever knew me anyway." So he was tutored at home and came to our program for group therapy and our art class. He turned out to be a first-rate painter and sculptor when he was able to pull himself together to work. When I got to know him, I learned about his family life.

Brad's father is a well-known scientist. To his family, he is known as an alcoholic. This is the main reason his wife recently left him. For years, when he went on a drinking binge, he would come home late at night, awaken the whole family and force them to endure endless accusations, everything from leaving light bulbs burning to plotting to get rid of him. Many times he beat Brad's mother before the children's eyes, and when Brad tried to interfere he would beat him as well. Brad stood up to his father on these occasions more than the other two children. He was the oldest. He became his father's prime antagonist trying to protect his mother who seemed to permit this sort of abuse year after year without doing anything about it. By the time he ran away into the West Coast drug scene, things at home had become unbearable:

*Father*: "My parents favored my brother and sister over me. I have always had the hardest time. Now I have this wife who never gives me the love and attention I deserve. You can't trust anybody in this world. My kids are lazy and they give me nothing. Not one thought of doing well in school, becoming *somebody* in the world, to give some sort of satisfaction to their father. Brad is a bad investment. He is never going to shape up. I'll be damned if I'll throw good money away for so-called therapy for that useless hippie. All those psychiatrists are ready enough to take my money, but where are the *results?*"

*Mother*: "I don't know how all this mess happened. When I

married him, I thought he cared for me. But he wanted so much attention and endless love. He seemed to care only about what he was *getting*—and the drinking! I'd have left him years ago if I thought I could make it on my own or if anyone else really wanted me. I guess I'm weak to have put up with all this for so long. I thought I was doing the right thing but when I saw what was happening to Brad, I knew I'd better leave that man. I don't want the other kids to be subjected to his drunken rages any more. If I hadn't left, I think Brad and his father might have killed each other!"

**Brad**: "My whole life has been the story of hating my father. He used to come home and beat mother up, and if I tried to stop him he would beat me up too. I remember lying in my bed at night listening to him screaming at her. I didn't know what to do—get up and get my head pounded or lie there dreaming how I would get a gun and kill my father. I guess he is the reason I am so angry inside. Once in Haight-Ashbury I bought a gun from a guy, and carried it in my pocket. I roamed around the streets just *hoping* some square would come along and give me a bad time! *Especially* a cop or some establishment cat in a business suit. For once I'd come out on top—I'd pull out the cannon and very deliberately I would shoot him till the gun was empty. Then I thought I'd feel peaceful at last. When I came down from the drug high, I saw how dangerous it was. I knew it was all the stored-up hate for my father that made me hope for a chance to kill someone. So I gave away the gun. I feel like a failure, a drug-head. Only drugs like heroin make me feel peaceful. On a drug I don't think of hating and killing, for a little while.

"People are probably all phony. On the surface they may seem respectable and all that. But underneath they are rotten. Businessmen steal, scientists make pollution and H-bombs, everyone lives on someone else's misery. I know I have some talent in art, but it's hard to concentrate on making things when the world is so full of hate and you feel so worthless inside."

Like Betsy, Brad went almost unnoticed in his terribly disturbed family until his psychotic breakdown following his drug episodes forced his parents to take time out from their own marital and personal problems at least for awhile. But it became clear that as soon as Brad left the hospital, he was going to have to return to the chaotic home scene with his mother, who was divorcing his father. She felt helpless to handle her own problems, let alone those of Brad who, shaken by psychotic fantasies and paranoid panic, needed someone strong and stable to lean on until he could evolve a life of his own.

The tragedy of Brad is one of lost potential. He is extremely intelligent and supremely creative. He writes, paints, plays guitar. His painting was strong and exciting as early as age ten. I've seen some of his work of that era, and it shows enormous talent. But as with Betsy, the family problems were so destructive that survival was the main concern, not development. What could Brad have done with themes other than hate? For him, too, neither public schools nor hospitals had given him a relationship with a single adult who meant much to him. Until he came to the School, his identification figures were famous poets and rock musicians he "knew" in fantasy only, by their work. He was actually intimate with no one.

### CHESTER: "WHERE, WHERE, WHERE TO BEGIN?"

At nineteen, Chester quit college after his freshman year. He found it intolerable to study subjects that were required for a "liberal arts background" taught by teachers he could not respect as people. He had lived in a dormitory there but he had only a couple of friends. He became more and more solitary, going into the basement of the college buildings to play his flute in the dark. He wanted to write something about man's condition on earth, about himself; he made endless starts on this, but when he reread any of it, it seemed worthless, so he tore it up. He began drinking a lot to cure his increasing feelings of depression. Finally he quit school and came home.

Chester came to see me on the suggestion of his mother. She is a nervous, prim little woman, who took care of Chester all his early years when a congenital malformation of his legs meant he had to be in a body cast for many months. He lay in bed in his cast, lonely and bored, and she tried to amuse him by reading to him or playing the piano. Whenever he needed anything she got it for him. She made herself his nurse for several years, from the time Chester was two years old till he was four and able to get back to normal activities. She always worried thereafter about Chester's frailty and his problems—his moodiness, friendlessness, erratic school work, then later his drinking and leaving college.

Chester's father is a hardworking, honest lawyer. Brought up in rural New England, he reminded me of Vermont farmers and Maine lobstermen I have met—straightforward, down to earth, concrete. He told me he had never gotten close to Chester whose dreamy philosophical nature had baffled him. "And back when he was little and got fresh or did something naughty, when I'd want to give him some real old-fashioned discipline, my wife would get so flustered at me. She was worried I'd hurt the boy with a slap or two. She treated him as if he were made of china. I guess I shouldn't have, but I gave up trying to be a father to him, and let her more or less bring him up. Now that he's nineteen, I don't understand him. I can't communicate with Chester, and I don't get the meaning of the stuff he writes either. I see he's in pain and I'd like to help him, but I can't see how to do it."

Chester presented himself to me as a kind of guerilla fighter on the frontier of man's existential dilemma. He would appear late to our interviews unshaven, dirty, sometimes hung over. He would wander around the basement of my office building, finding things to read on odd shelves and in corners. He found it hard to talk about himself, but easier to talk about "man." He told me his "theory of duality":

"It is man's duality that has brought him suffering and death and an eternal torture! Man can't achieve perfect goodness or evil. Dualities tear him apart inside. So he is condemned to drown in his own duality. I conceived of an Ungod—he is all the evil, the *bad* side of the duality. He would destroy the world, screaming. . . .

"Spontaneity transcends duality—it just *happens*. Duality is only in men's minds if they stop to think, to apply a value judgment. A spontaneous action comes *before* a value judgment is ever made on it. The value judgments never catch up to a spontaneous action.

"I want to be the *creative destroyer*, the Ungod! I want to create *spontaneously*, but I don't know what to say. Where, where, where to begin?"

Someone like Chester would be called a "borderline psychotic" and would almost never find a setting in which he could find some way to channel his brilliance and creative energy through the chaos of his bottled-up aggression and self-hatred, into constructive self-expression. The School had to be flexible and tolerant to permit Chester a long period of testing us out, seeing how much of himself we could stand. Yet we had to be able to communicate to him that we cared about him. At the School Chester could start out by getting close to me and to those few other students and teachers he felt safe with, people who would not demand too much of him, but not reject him either. He needed us to be different from his parents, who seemed to see only the issues of discipline versus spoiling. At the School we focused upon Chester's absolute uniqueness, we were impressed with his ideas. We liked him. That is why he stayed with us and eventually worked out some of his deepest problems with us.

PATTY: "I WANT TO BE WHERE THE ACTION IS."

At fifteen, Patty was smoking pot whenever she could get it. She was also having sex whenever she could get it and doing poorly in school. From the beginning, Patty was fun to work with: she was always honest, outspoken and dramatic. She gave me graphic descriptions of her mixed-up life, of her feelings of loneliness and frustration in her disturbed family, and her impulsive attempts to find affection and meaning in life with some boy she hardly knew or on a drug trip. As we worked together and she began to trust me, Patty got better control over herself, but her real improvement came when she joined our drama class, where she could act out and express her deepest feelings. The story, as it unfolded, revealed Patty and her parents expressing these points of view:

**Mother:** "Patty is a lot like me. She will suffer at the hands of men like I have. My father was psychotic. He would go into his crazy rages at home, and my mother not only tolerated them, but made us all act as if everything was all right. Why wouldn't she ever admit he was insane and get him into hospital? She acted as if taking care of him was a Christian martyrdom that she had to endure, as if she had no choice.

"I got married to get out of that house. I didn't know what a *loving* man was. I never met one. Wouldn't you know my husband turned out to be one of the most selfish, stingy, angry bastards in the world? I tried to handle him the way my mother handled my father, by turning the other cheek. When it got too much for me, I had nervous breakdowns. I've been in the mental hospital four times over the past ten years. It's the only vacation I get! Then I go home to him, and we start all over again. Don't ask me why I don't divorce him; I suppose I'm too dependent. Where would I go?

"Sex with him is terrible. I get so frustrated and he's so disappointing. When he fails in that department I sometimes let him know what I really feel about him! All I put up with and can't even get satisfaction so I can fall asleep! I don't see what Patty sees in sex to make her go after it so. It's a trap, like the rest of married life."

**Father:** "I was raised in a loveless family. Nobody gave anything to anybody. My parents died when I was about six, and I was brought up by a widowed grandmother and her sister. They were really stingy—characters out of Dickens: Turn out all the lights and eat as little as possible!

"When I got married I had no hope of my wife being any better than any of the old women who brought me up. As I look back I see that I didn't let her love me. I felt she must be trying to get something out of me—money or something. I guess I had learned that you never should let anyone get a grip on you, make you need them. Whoever you need has got you—you're hooked. So I kept control of everything, or tried to. Marriage has been a war for me, even sex. I distrust sex. Women frighten me. Patty is sexually aggressive like her mother. She tries to use men to give her what she wants. The man is unimportant—never mind what *he* wants. These women just attract you so they can get their own satisfaction.

"At least I'm good at my work. When people want to know about computers around here, they have to come to me! My phone rings all day. I have what they need and they have to meet my conditions or I don't give advice. At work I'm the king. I'd rather live in my office—that's where I feel good."

*Patty:* "My parents are the worst! I am sick of hearing them fight. It's been going on as long as I can remember. Why don't they get a divorce? Each time they threaten each other about divorce, I hope they'll finally do it. We might get some peace around here.

"My mother can be such a baby sometimes. I mean, I know she cares for me and the other kids, but she does it all as though she's bucking for a medal! I don't like to feel like part of her *burden*, for God's sake! Your love life should be a *pleasure*; if I think being with a boy will be *fun*, I go with him and I enjoy it. I guess some boys have used me—I mean they don't care who I am so long as we have sex. I know it would be better to make love to someone who really cared for me, but I don't feel many boys really like me. I don't think I'm good enough to attract the most interesting boys. Anyway, they are too square—just want someone to talk to about their college plans and stuff. I want to be where the action is! Right now, that means black guys!

"My father's worse than my mother. He does *nothing* for us. It takes a week to get a dollar out of him. He doesn't know what love is. If he talks to me for ten minutes, he acts like he should be elected father of the year!

"My real problem is willpower. When I get mad at my parents, I just say to myself 'What the hell! I don't get any appreciation at home no matter what I do anyway! They blame me for things no matter what I do, so why not go ahead and do what I want, I won't get treated any worse for it.' Of course, that's all just an excuse to make me feel justified doing what I feel like—sex or an acid trip or something. Then later I feel bad and I deserve to be punished. But of course I don't tell my parents, and they usually don't know what's going on. And that's my life."

For Patty, like for Chester, the School was the first environment she found in which she could survive and find out who she was. At home she was constantly provoked by her parents' battles into revengeful acting out of all kinds of feelings, mostly "You can't stop me from doing whatever I please," and "Do you love me even if I'm bad?" Trapped into these repetitious maneuvers, she would very likely have ended up with a child or two to care for or as a prostitute or married to some angry man who would abuse her as her mother was abused. Any psychiatrist has seen many examples of how such family situations lead to these outcomes. But Patty found that we would listen to her patiently, praise her for her talents in theater and dance, yet we would show her how angry retaliations against her parents were getting her into worse trouble. As with Chester, the combination of acceptance with helping the student see how the old patterns are destructive tends to help the student choose new styles of behavior, which the School can reward. It has something to do with finding

*The School We Have*

the Me inside the student—the Me which is not just made up of action and reaction in relation to a disturbed family situation.

### CHRIS: "MAYBE THERE'S NO ME AT ALL."

Chris was twenty when he came to see me. He had lived away from his parents for a couple of years. Because they lived far away, I never got to talk to them about Chris's early life. So his comments and memories make up most of what I know about his parents.

Chris was a brooding and angry boy, but powerful. He had rebelled and taken his position outside of most social institutions long before he came to see me. It could not be a total accident that Chris, the most pronounced rebel among my patients, came from the most prominent family of all. His father is chairman of the board of one of America's most famous corporations, and his mother is a daughter of one of America's first families. Chris remembers being brought up by a series of competent servants, who took care of him and his five brothers and sisters quite skillfully. But he could never get close to either his mother or his father. By the time he reached his midteens he was dropping out of prep schools and running away. Later he couldn't find any job that interested him. He got arrested once for dealing in pot and under probation came into psychotherapy and into our art and drama groups.

*Chris:* "Life so far for me has been a bummer. I mean I feel depressed for weeks or months at a time, so that I can't even get much out of smoking pot. Then I have these up phases when I feel all my problems are gone, and all I need is this chick or some money and everything will be alright. But even as I feel these things, I sort of know it's phony. I'll get depressed again and feel hopeless and worthless, and it will all be like it always was.

"My father is a phony; I've known it since I was small. He was going up the ladder in his business so fast he couldn't spare the time for us. He bought care for us. Why didn't he wait till he made it, then buy a set of grown-up children, all married and successful already? I never got to talk to him. When we had a few minutes together, he'd either scold me for something I did, or there would be a polite conversation about some trivial things. He paid more attention to some of the others, mostly the girls—they knew how to play up to him, I guess. I consider my father as a perfect symbol of the establishment I hate—dry rot at the top of society. In the chairman's chair, and he's a robot as far as I can tell.

"My mother is just like he is in her own way. Last year after we hadn't seen each other for a whole year, when I came home for Easter her first words were 'Don't think we can go anywhere with you unless you get a haircut!' She always liked the parties and social stuff that went with my father's jobs and didn't go in much for taking care of us herself. You know the maids could do it! Actually, if I didn't become the black sheep, I doubt if my parents would ever have found out who I was. I suppose I got them to notice me by being a misfit, the guy who wouldn't fit into the prepared future—college, graduate school, then business or one of the professions.

"I wish I had known my grandfather better; I have his name, and I think maybe I inherited his temperament. He was a swinger—had a few wives, made and lost a few million. I met him a couple of times, and he liked me. He seemed *real* compared to my father. He seemed to be enjoying his life; maybe that's why his kids were embarrassed by him. He did what he *wanted*, not what was *proper!*

"My father would have been closer to me if I had gotten interested in some of the things he cared about, like skiing and golf. He sometimes took us skiing. But I never got any good at it. I liked horses and boats. Somehow I was always not what he wanted me to be, but I never let myself sell out by pretending to like the things I didn't like, even if my father would like me better for it. I was always suspicious of becoming *like* him, so I avoided his interests, and found myself enjoying the kinds of activities my grandfather was interested in. When I get depressed, I sometimes wonder if I am not *me*, maybe there's no *me* at all, maybe I'm just trying to become my grandfather by doing what I heard he liked to do—sailing and riding.

"I want to get out of this phony society completely. When I can get my hands on some money, I'm going to buy a ranch some place—maybe Montana or Wyoming, and raise horses. I don't want any profit, I just want to keep on doing what I like. I haven't had much luck with girls: I always get mixed up with the screwed-up kind. My last girl was always cutting her wrists. A lot of my girls have been like me—running away, depressed, hating their families. So I don't count on getting married; it ties you down to someone who you probably couldn't trust anyway. I'll bring some friends into my ranch. We can live communally, work together, keep things *simple*. We'll grow some of our own food, make our furniture, build our house. Possibly we'll be able to be honest and open with each other and find some trust. I know one thing: I'll never live like my parents do if I have all the money in the world!"

Chris presented some of the problems that Chester did. He was terribly angry at his parents and at society, yet also felt worthless at his core. But Chris did not have the creative talents that Chester or Patty showed us, so we couldn't praise and reward those. He gave us almost nothing we could enjoy or relate to. He remained on the margin of the School as he had in his family, grim and critical, and eventually he slipped away from us without having made a solid connection. Chris worked with me in individual therapy for awhile, but whenever he had to look at himself in depth, he found it so depressing that he would stop coming to see me. If the School had been involved with an outdoor setting, like a ranch or a farm, we might have involved Chris more successfully. There has to be something to do that the student-patient really loves and respects. As for Chester and Patty and others, this activity can become the focus of a human relationship that builds and develops differently from previous relationships in his life, and shows him a new way to be.

VIC: "I CAN'T STAND THESE AUTHORITIES TELLING ME HOW TO LIVE."

Vic ran away from his middle-class home at fifteen. He returned home only when a probation officer ordered that he stay at home under the care of his parents. When a child runs away from his family so young, you might imagine that home is hell, as it was for Brad. And many kids run away from vicious homes like Brad's. But Vic described his home quite differently:

"Did you ever hear of Levittown? Well, this place was like that. A developer's heaven. Our house was one of the first boxes in the place. And it seemed that when they put up those phony towns near New York City, all the gang fights moved out of Brooklyn and the Bronx and came to the suburbs. I guess lots of people wanted to move their kids out of the bad slums where they were getting into trouble and fighting. So they came to these places that were quiet and had trees. They tore out the trees, flattened the place out and built all these boxes nearly alike. Then the gang fights and the stealing all moved out to the suburbs.

"I was a loser. I got picked on a lot. I never learned how to fight so I learned to run fast. Till I could run, I took a lot of beatings. Never just one guy—always a big gang. That's how they work. And that's how society works, too: they overpower you and force you to do what they want!

"My father was an architectural draftsman. He used to

*The School We Have*

bring work home sometimes in the evenings. He was conscientious and careful. I guess he was good at his work. He had a steady job with a big firm. Stayed there a lot of years. He was forty-three when he married my mother and about forty-six when I was born. I never knew about his life before they married, but once when I was about twelve or thirteen, I found some old papers that said he was married twice before. But he never told me anything about his life as a young man. We never could communicate anyway. Somehow we never knew each other—as people, I mean. He worked long hours. He would come home maybe seven thirty at night. He had to ride an hour and a half on the train to get to work in the city and an hour and a half to get home. So he left home before I got up for school and he got home about the time I went to bed. Sometimes he would work on his drawings in the evenings, or read the paper, or watch TV. He was tired all the time.

"He and my mother got along well, I think. They loved each other and I always thought they were happy together. There were no fights, no cold wars. They just did their jobs and seemed to be content with life. I didn't get close to either one of them, but I knew they expected me to go along peacefully like they did, do well in school, get a job, and make a home in some place like theirs.

"I started hating school after sixth grade. I had one or two teachers I liked and got good marks in those classes, but the average teacher was just doing it as a job to get paid—no enthusiasm, not caring. These classes were 'bummers.' I felt regimented, told I *had* to do this or that. But nobody told me why it was important to learn French or algebra.

"When I was fifteen I was crazy about motors. I had this outboard motor I wanted to keep in the attic but my mother said the gasoline would cause a fire. I told her I'd drain it and clean it, but no go. So I had to leave it in the yard and it got stolen, of course. It was then I decided to split. I saved about twenty dollars and one night I took off with the money and a paper bag of clothes. I went right to New York. On Forty-Second Street I found out you can make a lot of money hustling queers. They wanted me to play the male role, letting them blow me or balling them. I didn't feel particularly guilty. I stayed with guys I thought were good people. I learned a lot. I met some beautiful guys and some dirty old men too. I really cared about only one guy, a sailor who kept me for awhile. In a way he was like a good father—older than me and he could do stuff I couldn't do. He knew all about motors and boats and all.

"I got arrested for stealing once and had to go back home to live. The probation officer said, 'You'll be going to jail just as soon as I make the court complaint, after I get back from my vacation!' So I split to the city and found another queer to live with!

"I liked girls too, ever since I first had sex when I was twelve. I fell in love for the first time when I was eighteen. I had a job with a carpenter at the time. So I had money and I took her to live with me in a cheap hotel. The place turned out to be a junkie oasis, and that's where I learned how to shoot heroin. I dug it, but I've never been addicted. I'll do some smack [heroin] once in a while if I want to get high with other people who are doing it. At eighteen I was more of a needle freak than a heroin lover. I mean there was a kick, like a sex thrill, in using the needle.

"When my girl left me I felt depressed. That's when I broke up about three hundred morning-glory seeds with pliers and chewed them. That was my first psychedelic trip, and it was paranoid, just enormous fear. I turned on the gas, but I guess it wasn't poisonous enough. And I saw somebody slip a note under the door. It said, 'RENT TWO WEEKS OVERDUE. VACATE IMMEDIATELY.' I broke up laughing. Then I found a new chick and lived with her.

"I really loved Jeannie. Her parents insisted we get married, so we thought what the hell, its only a piece of paper, and we did. After about six months, we began having a few minor hassles—the kind I guess all married couples have. We both had some sex with other people then, and it really upset Jeannie. I had just taken it as sex, but chicks think it means more—they expect more communication out of it. Then her psychiatrist got into the act, advised her to leave me. That really got me upset. I can't stand these authorities telling me how to live. So I hit her; and that was more or less the end of our marriage. A little later I split for California."

Vic at twenty-four had become a dealer in drugs—LSD and marijuana. He had a girlfriend he cared about and plenty of money. But he remained depressed, he felt lost. He found himself trapped in an endless cycle of breaking the drug laws, getting caught, feeling trapped and desperate. Something inside him was making Vic a chronic outlaw, getting society to punish him. He had to find out why and change his life before he ended up in prison. When he came for therapy Vic was already facing court charges of drug dealing for the second time.

### DOM: "A PERSON IS RESPONSIBLE FOR THE WAY HIS LIFE GOES."

At fifteen, Dom was a street vagabond with very long dirty hair tied back with a leather thong, ragged clothes, and boots ripped open at the toes. He moved from one pad to another around Beacon Hill, panhandling and drug dealing. After a court appearance when he was picked up as a runaway, he was ordered by a probation officer to return home and to see the court clinic psychiatrist. The court clinic later referred Dom to me.

The home Dom was escaping from was chaotic. His mother had married young and had given six children to her husband, a Greek immigrant; she later complained she had not wanted so many kids but "he insisted." He was a firm and old-fashioned father, the real boss of the household until he died of a stroke when Dom was ten. From the start there seemed to be two kinds of sons in the family, those who went along with the father's discipline easily and those who rebelled. Dom was the oldest son and the most rebellious. He had many struggles with his father over household chores and even though he resisted giving in to his father's rules, he felt guilty about being such an antagonist to his father. When his father suddenly died, Dom felt he had been the main reason for his father's death. He developed the conviction that fate would somehow even the score, and he developed various phobias and obsessions to ward off this expected retaliation. Under the stress of this fear, he began using drugs, defying his mother's attempts to discipline him, and running away from home. Dom had to demonstrate to himself that he could do whatever he wanted and get away with it, but he feared that it would all catch up with him someday. Anything that smelled of anger or competition was particularly dangerous.

Dom was one of the most talented, creative kids I had ever met. After his first day visiting our School, he said, "I'm coming here every day and taking all the classes." And over a year's time he did try almost everything we offered. He found he had musical talent as well as painting and acting ability. He settled on sculpture, film-making, and drama and later guitar. To his own surprise he turned out to be an outstanding actor. He threw himself into dramatic improvisation with his whole spirit. His intensity was magnetic, at first even frightening—unconcerned over falling, he threw himself into movement problems, expressing feelings just as he felt them.

At first Dom tried aikido. The stress of aikido on spiritual peace through strength and confidence makes it popular with pacifists, especially boys who have always feared attack and avoided all possible violence. Knowing aikido, you know you have a *choice*—you don't *have* to flee, you *can* handle the situation. When Dom started aikido under our Japanese master, I was his partner. He was really afraid he might hurt me: "Promise you'll tell me right away if I start to hurt you!" And I promised. But still he couldn't make himself throw me down. We had soft mats on the floor, and we all had learned to fall properly, but Dom was not ready to risk hurting me.

After a crucial encounter in group therapy when Dom found out he was angry and frightened, he faced both group and individual therapy with impressive candor.

Dom had to come to terms not only with his mixed feelings about his dead father, but some very serious problems with his mother, who was scarcely twenty years older than he was. She was attractive and seductive and brought home lovers hardly older than Dom.

*Dom:* "I get into these gross situations with my mother. I think a lot of her style running the family is vague and weak and wrong. A lot of what she wants us kids to do is just to make *her* life easier and not to help us learn more about who we are and how to express ourselves. She's always laying her problems on us—how busy and tired and lonely she is! But we didn't do that to her! I think a person is responsible for the way his own life goes: if you don't want a certain style, then don't live that way. You've got to do what feels right to you!"

So Dom fled home where he felt seduced and ruled by his mother. What he found away from home was that culture of kids who like himself found living at home intolerable and set up a vagabond existence heavy with pot and LSD. Until he came to us, Dom knew of no other path.

### WANDA: "JUST FUCKING IS NOT ENOUGH."

Wanda is a strikingly beautiful black girl, tall and graceful. When I met her at sixteen, she was already very depressed and critical of herself. Her father was a successful engineer and her mother a social worker, and the family had moved a couple of years ago into an all-white suburb, leaving the ghetto behind. But only their material problems had been solved. Wanda's father did not love her mother and stayed away from home as much as he could. The mother wept, complained, but kept hanging on and hoping. The effect of years of this martyrdom was visible in Wanda and her sister Grace. Much like her mother, Grace made relationships in which she suffered and felt helpless, sometimes trying suicide. Wanda had adopted a more revolutionary attitude. If mother's values lead to suffering, overthrow them! Don't depend on people, do what you want to do, whatever you feel like. Don't let anyone make you suffer. But time and again her underlying sense that she was doomed to suffer like mother revealed itself. Her "liberated" promiscuity led to a pregnancy. Abandoned to her own solution, she went through a traumatic abortion. Her relationships always seemed to end badly.

*Wanda:* "You just can't trust people, particularly guys. They act like they love you, but if you won't fuck them, they take off. And if you do, afterward they don't seem to love you any better. They will find some other chick and disappear. Fucking is fine, but fucking is not enough! I want someone who really cares for me, but I have never found that someone. I don't think I ever will!"

Wanda's disillusionment, probably born out of her parents' loveless despair, found fertile ground in the ills of our society. She harnessed her anger to causes—the Black Panther party, women's liberation. Till she joined our community she could not believe people could be trusted to give anything to one another, or to care about each other without ulterior motives. It has been a hard lesson for Wanda to learn that there is a third path for a woman, neither suffering at the hands of men like her mother and Grace, nor rejecting her femininity with revolutionary ardor, but simply admitting her feelings and wants and finding people and situations where she can ask for and get what she wants.

# 6 › Teachers

I HAVE BEEN WONDERING how to describe the kinds of people who have become teachers at the School We Have—what qualities we look for, what we expect of a teacher, how our best teachers get involved with the students. And I find it hard to formulate these ideas. But recently, at one of our monthly staff meetings at my home, the special qualities which our teachers have in common were brought to light.

Both my wife and I have come to look forward to these meetings, which invariably work up to a great creative ferment. Someone has an idea and the inventive fantasies that follow are incredibly exciting. This particular meeting was no exception. We started off with Lois bringing up an issue which she had already discussed with some of the teachers—the problem of ungraded classes, where beginners and advanced students are taught together. How can she keep the advanced dance students progressing and learning some technique while giving the beginners improvisation problems they can handle? Most of the other teachers have similar problems to solve in their own classes. And we have been so limited in time, space, and money that we simply couldn't pay teachers more money to give us more of their time and thus to divide a dance or painting class into beginning and advanced sections and holding them separately.

Early in the meeting, I told the staff about our very limited progress in applying for grants from various agencies like the Massachusetts Department of Mental Health (Drug Rehabilitation Division), the state Department of Youth Services (Delinquency Prevention Program), and the Massachusetts Council for Arts and Humanities. If we get funds we can pay teachers more money and maybe even hold some advanced classes in the teachers' own studios. The money problem stems from our basic policy that no one is refused admission to the School for lack of money. Hence a couple of students with affluent parents pay from fifty to eighty dollars a week to attend, the average student pays thirty, and over one third pay five, ten, or no dollars a week. This fee buys all the classes a student wants to take, plus group therapy and psychodrama therapy. Since we pay teachers at the rate of fifty dollars a week for three teaching hours (plus two hours of attending group therapy with their students), the School is chronically broke. We discussed all this, as well as the fact that we are now becoming a nonprofit corporation so as to be able to seek outside financial help on a tax-free basis, and thus expand our program. In the meantime we came out with the kind of solution we usually find, namely, that teachers can design their own ways of meeting the problem within the time and money and space limitations we face. Some teachers decided to close their classes periodically to beginners and visitors. Others will work with advanced students on their own time. Some felt they could go on as they have been, juggling all levels at once. As I thought over this discussion, I realized how flexible and ingenious many of our teachers are; sensing the needs of their students, they adapt the classes to suit these needs.

After we reached this point in the discussion, someone brought up a new subject. Bob and Ildre, our psychodrama group leaders, plan to get married this summer and I have offered them the use of my home and the woods around it for their wedding. They have invited everybody at the School to come to the wedding. So we spent the next hour talking about this event and it became clear that this wedding is going to turn into a creative happening. Various staff members offered to involve themselves and their classes in putting up a wedding pagoda or tepee; playing rock, blues, chamber music, and African drums; making marriage robes out of batik-dyed fabrics, and so on. This wedding will turn out also to be a celebration of the School's existence. The date will be set by our astrologers, say Bob and Ildre.

As the meeting began to break up someone started to talk about Louisa, one of our students, who has come out of her deep depression recently and begun to feel good about herself. Soon everyone was involved in reviewing Louisa's progress at the School. As one teacher after another told how they had been involved with her, what I could hear was the story of how the School lets each teacher find his own ways of being useful to a student.

The first one to get to know Louisa had been me. About a year ago she came and asked me if she could join. She was a stocky girl of eighteen, hiding her body in loose ragged shirts and jeans, wearing men's hiking boots. Her face was always hidden behind her long hair and you could rarely see her looking directly at you. Louisa had a hard time talking, speaking with great hesitation and forcing her way past some inner block with each sentence. I didn't ask her much about her life at first because she was still seeing another psychiatrist, and liked him. Louisa wanted to continue that therapy. She liked to paint and wanted to start with an art class. From her therapist I learned that Louisa was born with a congenital lung disease resulting in chronic, serious lung infections and other complications. A child born with this disease suffers great pain and disability and can die of infectious complications, often pneumonia. Louisa's family somehow never knew she had the condition until Louisa was fourteen, though she had years of recurrent infections. She recalls her mother as unable to tolerate her demands for attention to her physical discomfort, pushing her aside, taking her to doctors only after long periods of worsening illness. Her parents' marriage had never been satisfying to either, and her mother felt trapped with the burden of raising four children without much love or emotional help from her absentminded husband, who withdrew from her anger and frustration into his work and was "mentally never home." She never could appreciate Louisa's uniqueness as a creative child and her trenchant bitter honesty.

So Louisa grew up, fleeing from one boarding school to another, finding from teachers in those schools only the rejection and betrayal she had already become conditioned to expect from her experiences at home. It took her months of silence in group therapy before she dared finally to reveal herself, and her first comments were bitter: "Why trust anybody? Everyone uses you. No one really cares. When I was sick, my mother didn't want to hear about it. At first I was glad to escape to schools, just to get away from *her*. But I couldn't stand the people at those places either. When I got to be fifteen, an art teacher of mine acted interested in my work. I couldn't believe it, I was amazed. How could he like the crap I was doing? But I started to believe him and to think I could do *something* right. Then I found out it was just sex he wanted, just to use me, and afterward he just stopped noticing me at all!"

Yet there was something so appealing and powerful beneath all this bitterness that various teachers at our School wanted— and tried—to help her. She puts everyone through the test of her readiness to be rejected or misused. Her first encounter with her first painting teacher at our School was like the others in the past: Louisa showed him her work, found his comments too critical, and was deeply wounded. But this time Louisa brought the incident up in the group therapy with the teacher present. After revealing her despair and her anger at the teacher, she was able to let him and later other art teachers help her to prepare work for application to be admitted to a first-rate art school. To her amazement, she was accepted. She told the group about this as if the school had made a mistake in taking her, but for the first time some pride in herself was visible in Louisa's attitude. And each time she talked, Louisa kept getting back the same message from the therapy group: "You see, you *can* make it. People here have helped you. You are going to do better work if you let people help you, get to you. Some people *can* be trusted!" Around this time Louisa made approaches to Mary, a teacher and counselor on our staff. Mary is an energetic and sympathetic woman of fifty who is married to a business management consultant. Creativity runs high in Mary and her family, which on the surface looks "straight" Concord. Mary's husband is a first-rate actor, Mary plays viola, and her oldest son is an artist. Louisa found Mary willing to sit over coffee with her for hours, accepting and hearing what she wanted to say. Through Mary, Louisa felt she had a place to go, and got closer to Mary's artist son as well as the whole family. One rarely gets this amount of time and closeness from a professional therapist.

Now Louisa started to feel safe in revealing herself more to me. She was finishing her therapy with her psychiatrist, who she now felt was pushing her out prematurely from his care. She asked me to see her instead, and I agreed. She also joined the weekly yoga-meditation class which I teach, and became a very devoted and hardworking student, exactly as she turned out as a patient. The basic themes of Louisa's therapy were her self-disgust and feeling of worthlessness. More and more she started to see that she had adopted what she felt were her mother's deepest feelings about her. Later in talking to her mother, I came to agree that there was much in this mother's despair with her own life and her marriage which probably infected Louisa's early feelings with despair and loneliness.

The realization that her feeling of worthlessness was a product of her family situation and not an immutable fact, was a turning point for Louisa. Now she exposed herself further: she started attending Lois's dance classes where she worked hard and took the risk of looking ridiculous and

*Teachers*

clumsy, as she struggled with modern-dance technique and improvisation. And it didn't make it any easier for Louisa that our only dance studio is a big open space which can't be closed off from the view of students from other classes and visitors who flock to the School each Saturday. Lois refers to her class as "the Saturday afternoon floor show." But Louisa made herself stick it out.

Then she joined our psychodrama therapy series. Bob and Ildre are the leaders. I had met them through friends and I had seen them work with psychodrama. They are two incredibly sensitive and talented people. When I think in generalities about our staff, I like to believe that we hire teachers and therapists who are absolutely first-rate, who are "where it's at" in their fields. Bob and Ildre are masters at using drama techniques to help people unmask deep feelings about life situations that trouble them. We set up psychodrama as an elective kind of group therapy, held at the same time as the group therapy meetings I lead. Students who wish to join have to sign up for an entire psychodrama series of twelve weekly sessions and a two-day weekend marathon. To my surprise, Louisa plunged into this and again stuck it out. Anyone who knows psychodrama with an expert leader knows how intense and moving it is. But I knew Louisa now, and I could trust Ildri and Bob to handle her feelings tenderly yet honestly. They did. Louisa found she could use psychodrama to help herself, and now also to help others. The climax came when one evening Louisa invited her group to meet at her house, where they found her, in Ildre's words, "a gracious and relaxed hostess. And her paintings all over the walls, where we could all see them, were wonderful! It was clear that she trusted us."

Sometime in this period, Louisa decided to take a mescaline trip with a girlfriend. Even though this friend has had a lot of experience with psychedelics and is a loving person, I am sure that had I been consulted beforehand, I would have advised Louisa strongly not to do it. I have seen long-term bad effects after mescaline trips, and I would have been concerned lest Louisa's deep depression and anger surface and overwhelm her uncertain new strength. But it is not Louisa's style to ask advice, and she took the trip. In retrospect, I am glad she did. She saw and felt two vital aspects of her life that day, her relationship to her disease and her body, and her deepest feelings about her mother. For eight hours or more Louisa experienced herself:

"I felt my hatred for my body, how disgusting and loathsome I have always felt my body is. I could *feel* what my disease did to me, made me feel so ugly and hate myself. But for the first time I feel that it's not *me* who is bad, it's the disease. *I* can be worthwhile, I can like myself. I see how I've let my body go, I've misused it. I felt, 'What the hell, it's no good anyway!' And I was my mother looking like a witch. I felt my mother's hatred for my disease and for her marriage and having children and her whole ruined life!"

Since the mescaline trip, Louisa has seemed changed—less depressed, less bitter. She is more open now, feels more worthwhile than before. And now she is beginning to feel like a woman, to feel that there is even something to be hoped for in a relationship with a man. She has been able to deal effectively with a roommate who had become a problem to her. For months she had put up with the situation, but now Louisa found she could tell her roommate that their life styles were so opposed that she really preferred to live alone; the roommate left. This is a kind of action Louisa could never have taken before, during the long years of self-hate. She would have fled the situation herself, and felt she was the failure.

But the process of teachers finding ways to help a student did not end there. The last voice raised at the end of our meeting was David's. He is a young scientist in his twenties who teaches science seminars for us—on human reproduction, nutrition, brain functioning, drugs and your mind and body, ecology, cosmology, and so on. David had gone through some exciting changes in psychodrama at the same time as

Louisa. He discovered feelings in himself, he explored them and became comfortable with them. David came to know Louisa in their psychodrama group. On his own, he studied the subject of Louisa's disease. He now asked me for advice on how to use this information to help Louisa. He found out that the vital thing for Louisa is to care for her body well—with early care of infections, with breathing exercises, and so on. David feels love for Louisa and he will counsel her, discuss her disease with her directly and honestly in a way that all her doctors have been unable to.

As the teachers began leaving the meeting, Dick added a footnote about Louisa's work in his painting class. He described a change in Louisa:

"Louisa used to draw with us from the model, but her vision was all in her own head. I would get something down from my way of seeing the model, the others would put down their visions of the model, but Louisa's was always her own, not of the model at all. She wasn't recording what effect the model had on her, but something from her inside, something exciting and special, but her own experience, not with us, not together looking at the same model. Last week we sat there again in front of the model, and some really new thing began to happen. Louisa was taking in the model and putting out a vision that was related to the model, that showed she was there with the model and with us. Because she's really with us now."

Since then Louisa has even substituted for her painting teacher and taught a painting class successfully. Her students also felt she was here with them.

As a result of experiences like Louisa's, we know we can't define abstractly what we are looking for in a teacher, then go out and find these qualities. Dick's teaching style differs from David's as much as his life style does. And our teachers are a very varied bunch. Some of them are married, live in the suburbs, own two cars and television, send their kids to college. Some on the other hand live unmarried with their "old man" or "old lady" or alone in some loft or studio, owning practically nothing. Their ages range from eighteen to over fifty. Some work full-time for straight institutions like universities, and some have little or no visible means of support. Some have taken lots of drugs, others would not smoke pot if it were given away free. One of our teachers started out with us three years ago as a student, a delinquent high school dropout. But the Louisa story reveals the common quality all share—they are *available* as feeling human beings, not only as teachers. They are available to the students, with whom they share not only classes but group therapy. And here I thank my intuitions which told me at the beginning that one basic feature of the School should be that students and teachers should be involved *together* in group therapy. Of course you can pay a teacher for his time, for the hours he spends in the group each week, but you can't buy emotional availability. The teacher must be available *as a person*. And we have been able through the group process to help teachers become more available. Anyone who has been in a well-led therapy group knows the tremendous intimacy and involvement that evolve when a group *works*. To find this intimacy between a student and his teacher is to me the core of all education.

At first we sought out teachers who were old friends, like June, who has been an actress for ten years. We knew her work and her emotional reliability. Then as group therapy progressed, the exposure to the atmosphere of honesty helped June become freer to express her own feelings directly to her students, feelings like anger and dissatisfaction, which she had tended to avoid showing. When we found Dick, our art teacher, we found an incredibly free-wheeling man, one who encounters every new situation amazingly unencumbered by obligations from others. His energy and imagination seem boundless. Working with anything and anyone at hand, he can make students *see*. The group involvement has had its effects on Dick, different from its effects on David and June. Dick has come to be more aware of his responsibility to the students. It has had a similar effect on David (not the same David who teaches science), who, as I pointed out earlier, was first brought to us by a student named Don who wanted to study blues and jazz piano with him. Since then, David for a long while became our "music department" and a mainstay of the School. Many professional musicians come to sit in with David and our students. Now David teaches a music theory class as well for his more advanced students. David has taken up some of his own work problems with us in the group and has also dealt there with the opinions of students about how he runs his classes.

David has now had two young students as "apprentices" at the School. Both relationships developed, neither was ever labeled as a formal training arrangement. The first such master-apprentice relationship with Don is a vivid illustration of the unusual role of the teacher at our School. Don came to us in his early twenties, depressed and quite paranoid, veteran of at least four serious attempts at therapy. As I mentioned in Chapter 3, Don brought David to us as a teacher: "There's this guy who plays blues piano. He's really where it's at musically. I'd like him to be my teacher." He brought David to see me; David was hired, and he's stayed with us for three years. Don not only played piano in the blues jams with David, but he arranged for long intense private piano lessons with him, and was also in individual therapy with me. He developed a very intense and ambivalent relationship with David, admiring him musically but supersensitive to any hint of mistreatment, just as he had been with his parents.

Don's father was a prominent surgeon; from the start he had been disappointed with Don's dreamy nonaggressive nature. He wanted his firstborn son to be alert, intelligent, interested in being like his father. This boy was more passive, a loner who liked music and drawing pictures. He was not someone that this father could relate to. A lot of this family's pleasure in having a child was in relating his achievements to friends. This prominent family highly social and politically influential, giving big parties where the best people attended—a *Vogue* magazine social life. Don's mother had hundreds of dresses, coats, shoes, purses. She was more creative herself than her husband. She had done some painting and she liked to keep herself in the social life centering around the art museum, giving parties for artists and attending openings. Her taste in art and clothes was famous. But she couldn't relate successfully with Don either. He was sloppy, disorganized. He would wear the same T-shirt till it rotted on him. He left his things where they fell. And later, while his parents belonged to the Symphony Orchestra Association, he became fascinated with country blues, playing records of Blind Lemon Jefferson and Lightnin' Hopkins and John Lee Hooker, which sounded absolutely atonal to his parents.

Don failed first in the best private elementary schools, then even in the "special attention" private schools he was sent to in order to nurse him as far as college. In adolescence, all the old stored-up rage at his parents burst forth and he became severely depressed and for a while actually paranoid, with delusions of persecution. He had four years of intense psychotherapy, and finally was committed to a hospital and treated with electric shock, which resulted in a rock-hard crystallization of his attitudes against hospitals, doctors, shrinks, and the whole established order of society.

One interesting point is that I knew Don during this phase, when he was eighteen, a year after his shock therapy. During the year I had him in psychotherapy, I got almost nowhere with his basic feelings, and found it possible only to work as a mediator or translator between him and his parents, which made his life run more smoothly while he remained at home. But that was before the School was organized. Three years later, when the School began, Don came around and wanted to join. He had left home and was trying to live on his own, but he was pretty severely alcoholic and very depressed. So now I had another crack at Don as a patient, but this time with the help of David as his piano teacher and the School as the background. At the School, Don avoided revealing anything personal in group therapy. He lit up every time someone criticized their parents, or any school or job. He took the role of leader in a Greek chorus bemoaning how totally fucked-up society is, especially middle-class parents with their expectations and empty social posturing. In individual therapy I got the story of how his relationship with David was going. At first Don put David through one of the most paranoid and exasperating testing periods ever designed. He missed lessons completely, showed up drunk, didn't practice, used his lesson time to denounce society, parents, the School, David, music, life. David and I talked this over from time to time. I saw that David could understand Don's bitterness and rebellion. Himself a loner, alienated from most social structures, David could see Don's talent and possibilities. He didn't let himself be drawn into Don's game, he would not reject Don. Many times he scolded him, battled with him to face what he was doing with his life, and then hung in to face whatever came next in this stormy relationship. The result was that Don got better. He kept up with his lessons and improved his musical skills. His respect and love for David was evident in the way he talked about David in his therapy sessions with me. From a deeply despondent, depressed, paranoid state, Don started to change. He moved in with a girl he cared about, dealt with their problems as a couple. At that time we held some couple-therapy sessions when he felt we needed them. His piano playing improved, and David got him some dance-accompaniment jobs. His self-esteem went up.

What was evident to me was that without this combination of therapy and apprenticeship to a musician whose work he admired deeply, Don would certainly have failed to respond to any attempt to help him. Not only had Don failed to respond to psychotherapy before, even with the same therapist, but shock therapy and hospitalization had made him *less* accessible to psychiatric help, not more. The apprenticeship with David had resulted from Don's *selection* of David as someone who could relate to him, when just about nobody else could. He was right. David found him exasperating but worth helping. And their relationship gave Don an ongoing life experience of the greatest importance, which he could tell me about in his therapy sessions. Gradually he could come to understand what he was doing with David and with his life.

Because of his apprenticeship with David, Don had a better chance to relate constructively to the School and to therapy. I can talk to Don about his relationship with David and with music, using that relationship as a prime subject for discussion in psychotherapy. David has provided the same reality for two of his students: a teacher whose work is admirable, who cares about you, is patient with your mistakes, values you as a person and a future musician. In the costume of the blues-jazz life style, it is a master-apprentice relationship reminiscent of the guru-novitiate arrangements in zen and yoga. And it is most important that the atmosphere of the School permits and encourages such relationships between students and teachers, patients and therapists. In our setting, personal relationships are possible, they are common, they are encouraged by students and teachers attending the same therapy groups.

In the group therapy sessions, teachers can hold dialogues with students about their classes and how to make them better. But teachers can also bring up their life problems in the group, just as the kids do. For some time after we started our groups, there was a tendency for teachers to hold back discussion of their own problems in deference to the kids. As Lois put it, "After all, this place is for the kids." But I don't agree on that point. One of the greatest benefits of a staff-student group is the opportunity it gives the kids to see adults they respect actually confronting their own life problems and finding ways to overcome them. So I try to present my own problems and I encourage the staff to do the same. Gradually, they are doing it. And the development of skills in revealing how you feel, getting closer to people more honestly, is therapeutic for teachers no less than for the kids. I have been struck by the help it has given teachers in dealing with their own personal problems more honestly. One way we have been so successful in keeping teachers is the help they get by working in so emotionally open a setting.

Many free schools and drop-in-centers for adolescents use volunteers as teachers and counselors. We have tried it a few times and found it generally didn't work. When someone *gives* his time he must be exceptionally devoted to become involved in group therapy as well as teach. Our volunteers either could not get deeply enough involved or they finally became paid teachers. Paying a teacher well helps him support his own art or craft and his self-esteem at the same time. Since most of our staff are artists they share the chronic problem of finding money to live on while practicing their art. They don't want to waste time and energy on unrelated moneymaking activities. Getting paid for teaching their own arts helps them solve this one.

I have pointed out earlier in the book that in choosing teachers, we look for men and women already committed to their art or their profession. In too many schools the teaching of the arts is delegated to hobbyists or amateurs. In our School we do not ask a student to learn painting from someone who is not a painter, or to learn how to dance from a person who is not a dancer. We do not employ hobbyists as teachers, because we want the kids exposed to a *whole* painter or a *whole* dancer, complete with the life style, feelings, attitudes, and problems that go with the occupation. And through the relationship with this kind of teacher, the student learns not only ways to paint or dance, but what it means to *be* a painter or a dancer.

Within their own skill areas, our teachers are autonomous in the School. They arrange to get the needed materials (which the School pays for), set up their own teaching plans. Lois plans every class in detail, and has kept notes on every one. Dick, on the other hand lets the class situation move him whichever way feels right at the time. Carol, another art teacher (who has now gone to the Far East on a traveling fellowship) used to set up elaborate slide shows and classes in special art techniques requiring much advance preparation. As long as the teacher's style of preparation and working with the kids pleases him and his students, the School accepts his way of working. The process leads in its own way to its own kind of product, and the School respects that and does not interfere with any teacher's way of shaping his work with the kids. Occasionally a teacher's dissatisfactions come up in a staff meeting, and we talk about possible changes in method. Or the dissatisfactions of students about a teacher's way of working tend to come up in group therapy meetings, and changes can develop from there. So teachers are autonomous within their skill areas, but they get feedback from staff and students anytime.

One way the School has found new students has been to let interested kids come and take classes alongside enrolled students. Because of this, teachers have had to develop great flexibility to get something across in new and often unexpected situations. Groups of new faces appear. One such group came to Lois's dance class, were told to take off their shoes and take positions on the floor with the regular students. They worked out for two hours. Later Lois found out that her new students (she described them as "young men in generally terrible physical shape") were members of a seminar from MIT in "emerging life styles." A couple were social workers from a Cambridge counseling agency. In a recent group meeting the consensus of our kids was that casual visitors and "tourists" should be discouraged, but people who want to experience our School with the idea of enrolling should be allowed to come and take part as always. "And it's up to us to get to know them and make them feel welcome," said one student.

As to final selection of teachers, Lois and I as codirectors have that power. We encourage all kinds of personal involvement between teachers and students except sexual affairs.

Teachers have taken kids home, shown them their own studios and their work, introduced them to their own friends and families—occasionally teachers have even offered students a short-term home in a crisis. Sexual affairs between teachers and adolescent students are something else again. Whether or not people like to admit it, they tend to happen in all schools where there are adolescents. In most schools, these are more or less open secrets, officially secret but known of and talked about by many. This split between officially sanctioned behavior and what is *really* going on is opposite to the open spirit of our School. So when the inevitable rumors of so-and-so falling for so-and-so begin to be heard, we bring it up in group therapy and hear about the jealousies, the status problems, the disappointments, and all the rest. The result has been that these affairs happened no more after the first one or two have been discussed in depth.

Our teachers often find ways to turn crushes and more serious sexual advances into opportunities for insight and growth. Dick, the painting teacher, has discussed with me his relationship with Belinda. At fifteen she is a striking, tall, and energetic girl who radiates life and imagination. Belinda is still at that stage of awkwardness that precedes becoming a beautiful woman. All the ingredients are there. As Dick recalls:

"Belinda came to me directly—she wanted me to be her first lover. Not only her first sexual lover, her first lover, and she wanted me to help her be really sure it wouldn't be a failure. It was hard to say 'No, I won't be your controlled subject,' after I'd already reassured her I'd be her friend and she could say anything at all to me. Already I could see that she was almost magically under my control, ready to be under any spell of mine. I had to make her understand that I wasn't creating this situation, she was. She was stimulating herself from inside; these were feelings awakening in her. I could say to her, 'You feel horny today, it's obvious.' 'Yes,' she would agree. I'd think of ways to arrange some nonsexual encounter, because if I let it be in some intimate setting it could develop sexually. I talked about the Oedipus side of her wishes, and she understood. I tried to find ways to keep her growing, not to stop her growth by giving her emotional feedback, stuff to fantasy over. I would not advise her to leave home at fifteen and face the troubles of other kids who have had homes they couldn't stay in. So I helped her plan to stay in school and get ready for some kind of college. She'll soon be ready to find herself an old man to live with, learn to be someone's old lady—a lot of girls are doing that while in college."

As Dick talked to me about this, I recalled how at fourteen I had that kind of puppy love crush on an eighteen-year-old girl camp counselor. She treated me with sensitive skill. I came through feeling that although I couldn't be Rosalie's lover, soon I would be taken seriously as someone's lover. It was like a first fitting, and I look back on Rosalie's way of taking me seriously with great tenderness. Belinda will feel that way about Dick. It is not only the fact that he invests the time and energy to advise her, but that he takes her completely seriously as a person and lets her into his heart in a deep way.

Another bonus from the policy of full discussion relates to the search of adolescents for "identification figures"—to make older people into models whose values and behavior they can emulate as they figure out what kind of adults to become. Issues involving sex and love, dependency and responsibility, "using" people and respecting them have inevitably come up as we talked about a love affair—and this has thrown light on what kind of person the teacher *really* is, not merely what impression he wants to give of himself.

So in some ways we are a School, but we are a lot like a commune or a village. We are teaching human development as much as we are teaching art or music. Our sacrament is honesty. But unlike the villages of simpler societies, it is not merely the old teaching the young, not all one way. It is everybody learning from everybody. Recently a student suggested we start a "girls' group," where girls and women could talk to each other "about things you want to talk about without men around." The idea caught on, and for a time it became a weekly event. Unlike our group therapy and psychodrama, there is no designated leader. In describing the feeling of the group, which lasted a couple of months, Lois told me that everyone from fifteen to fifty seemed to have something valuable to contribute and that no one showed special deference to older members, Lois, or other teachers. In this lies the essence of the School We Have. Our staff are willing to meet the kids as equals, despite their greater life-experience.

# 7 › What Happens in Classes at the School

IN THE FIRST CHAPTER I described some events which took place when Bill, one of our music students, spoke for David, who had been his music teacher, at a staff meeting. In order to convey the nature and purpose of classes at the School We Have, I would like to pursue the story of how the School helped Bill to reach the point where he became a full-time music student. When he first came to the School, Bill was a quiet and reserved twenty-two-year-old who told me that he had graduated from Columbia in philosophy but ran out of gas after leaving college. He had not worked hard in college, but he read quite a bit, particularly in Far Eastern philosophies, becoming fascinated with yoga and zen and doing some meditation on his own. He didn't have to work hard at college to do well, and he regarded college as a kind of game, where you had social permission to live almost as you liked, reading and studying if you chose, putting in very short spurts of work toward the end of each semester and managing that way to get sufficiently high marks to stay in school. It kept you from having to think about work or what kind of a life you wanted for yourself, he told me. The problem was when he graduated, he didn't know what he wanted to do.

Bill's father is a very successful engineer. He reached executive level in his company years ago and has risen to national prominence as president of his engineering company. He is an aggressive man who works very hard and is hard on everyone around him. He expected a lot from Bill from the beginning, and was disappointed very early when Bill turned out to be reserved and dreamy, not a competitor. Bill's father didn't try to find much close involvement with Bill, who was the first of his three children. Bill can't remember a real conversation with his father, or even seeing him much during his childhood. Bill does recall the house where he spent the first six years of his life, a farmhouse near a river with trees and flowers. His mother liked gardening in those days and the place had a relaxed and natural feeling to Bill, who loved walking through the woods, throwing stones into the river. He came to enjoy his solitude. But for reasons Bill didn't understand they moved when he was about six, into a much bigger house in a suburb. No more nature. About that time Bill's father was making his climb into the highest brackets in the company, and he worked late most nights. Bill's mother must have felt his absence too, because she began getting depressed and using a lot of the sleeping pills her doctor prescribed. Bill can recall long hours of emptiness and quiet in the house after he came home from school, wondering where his mother was and what she was doing. He would go up to her door and listen, wanting to go in and tell her what he had been doing, talk to her about something. More than once he could hear her snoring, and once when he was about to knock on her door, searching for contact, he heard her slide off the bed onto the floor. She didn't wake up.

Bill's mother's depression became chronic, and his father's mood at home was generally irritable and angry. His father began drinking too many cocktails every evening. In this emotional desert, Bill grew up, becoming more and more reserved, a good student at school, but lonely and unable to make relationships with other kids. It was an empty life. He learned how to insulate himself against his feelings, which by now were pretty well repressed.

*The School We Have*

Before he reached college, Bill spent four years in a prep school of high academic standing, where he pursued his solitary way, with few friends. By the time he graduated, he had become a regular smoker of marijuana and hashish, and familiar with speed. In college he took a large number of psychedelic trips, LSD and mescaline, and became acquainted with the use of cocaine, which became his favorite drug. As he later explained, "Coke makes you feel your senses more intensely. People rub it on their genitals, it enhances sensation. When you snort it, you get a beautiful rush, you have great fantasies. It gives me more pleasure than acid. But coke drags you down—you lose weight, you don't eat, you don't know how exhausted you are."

So here was Bill, with cocaine becoming his most deeply *felt* experience, all the rest an intellectual exercise. Of life with people, of emotions, of shared activities, of creative experience, he was getting nothing. And in that shape he came to our School.

From the beginning, Bill took up music. First he experimented with flute, and Pat was his teacher. Pat is in his forties, a silver-haired Boston Symphony musician, master of flute, clarinet, saxophone. Pat has incredible patience, loyalty and perseverance. For about fifteen years, Pat has worked with delinquent kids, becoming assistant superintendent of the Massachusetts "maximum security" institution for the most seriously delinquent boys in the state correctional system. Within the Youth Service Department Pat had fought administrative and legal battles for years, trying to introduce and support creative programs and generally meeting with failure. But Pat did not quit. I came to know Pat when I was chief psychiatric consultant for the department (then a division). At that time Pat was being attacked politically for having refused to let a sadistic superintendent get by with abusing the kids in the institution, and he and I found ourselves on the same side during the hearings. From that point, my friendship with Pat developed, and I asked him to teach music at the School. He taught individual lessons in woodwinds, and of course became a member of the group.

Pat needed all his patience to deal with Bill because, while it became clear that Bill was talented, he was also terrified of responsibility and of the expectations of others. When Pat told him he was an exceptionally talented flute player, Bill found himself suddenly unable to practice and quit his flute lessons. All this time Bill was almost silent in the group therapy sessions and had not yet come to me for individual therapy. So it was not until later that he and I had a chance to talk in depth about his feelings when he discovered he could really become a flute player. Much later, when he was in therapy regularly, Bill told me that he was scared to death by Pat's praise. Something good would be expected of him, and how could he know if he could do it? What would people feel about him if he then disappointed them, and much worse, how would he feel about himself if he let himself expect something and then failed? He just couldn't stand to feel a tiny bit worse about himself, so the chance could not be risked. No flute.

Then Bill found a less threatening way to get into music at the School. He started getting interested in electric bass guitar, which fits into jazz, rock, and blues. David became interested in Bill, and every Saturday afternoon Bill would play bass guitar in David's jam session. Bill was learning by ear, picking up style from other bass players, and there was little pressure on him. David's style of running the jam was very soft-sell and permissive, and it seemed to make little difference if Bill were there or not. There was another student who already played bass, and this boy wanted more practice on guitar. So when Bill was around, this kid played guitar; if Bill didn't show up, there was a bass player anyway. And Bill slowly became friends with David, whose general approach to life was much like Bill's own. Bill got fascinated with blues, particularly black blues of the thirties and forties, which was

David's specialty. Together they would spend hours playing records of great old-time blues men, going to the clubs and bars where blues artists were playing. Bill became David's sidekick, then later, as he learned how to play better, one of David's sidemen. This relationship took place largely outside the School, and when David left his old lady, they began spending almost every evening together. So when Bill came to our staff meeting to speak for David about the problems of our music department, he was speaking for his closest friend and he knew he had David's support. This kind of relationship just would not have happened between a student and a teacher in most schools.

Bill gained confidence in his music. He became a fixture in David's jam, always there every week, always on time. Then one day he came to the group session in terrible shape. All the passivity and reserve were gone. He was red-eyed, trembling, close to collapse. He told me that he now realized that his drug problems were out of control. He had been doing cocaine for a week, plus lots of grass every day, and he had been experimenting with heroin. He was worried about his drug use; he needed drugs every day so as not to feel depressed and in despair about himself. He asked for intensive individual therapy. Since that time, we have been working together. I consider that Bill would not have reached the point of asking for more help unless he had already been helped so much by his relationship with David, and through him and Pat before him, with music at the School. Pat helped Bill see that he had unusual musical talent, and that had scared him. Then David had showed him how someone who was much like himself really *could* make his life as a musician. Bill wanted to become a musician badly enough now to risk exposing his long-buried feelings. He realized that in order to get it together to play music, he would have to gain control over his drug use and his other problems. "I want to be able to practice, to learn without giving up, to rely on myself to do the work. Not to *need* to be stoned. I want to get a girl to live with me and to be able to be close with her. I want to have feelings to play music *about*." Bill has stuck in therapy intensively, and now has enrolled in a professional music school as a full-time student. He is switching to string bass, which he considers a purer instrument than the bastard electric bass guitar, and he wants to be able to play pure music—advanced jazz, classical— to know what music is about, from the ground up.

In the days before the School, when I had nothing to offer someone like Bill except individual therapy, I often used to feel that at the close of therapy, I was saying to my young patients: "Now you know why you were hung up, why you suffered. You understand now why you were blocked from becoming who you wanted to be. Now therapy is over, so go out into the world and find ways to become what you want to be." But for someone like Bill, who can make it in college for four whole years without ever being reached by any living soul, this sort of a psychiatric commencement speech is useless. Kids like Bill need a very different sort of introduction into the world. To live in a style that expresses themselves, they need a kind of apprenticeship which simultaneously teaches artistic dedication and personal honesty. There are so many ways to hide from expressing yourself, because—like Bill—you are afraid you'll let yourself down or have nothing to say or be inept at saying it or for hundreds of other reasons. When your family life has not given you the self-awareness and confidence to believe in your own statement of yourself, you need to learn not only how to do something well, but also how to *live* life, not avoid it. That's what Bill is learning from us at the School in addition to music. His apprenticeship, in art and life together, is what classes at the School We Have are all about.

Highly creative kids are different from the merely intelligent. As Getzels and Jackson pointed out in their book *Creativity and Intelligence*, creatively gifted children are aware even before adolescence that they are different from their peers of equal intelligence in very important ways. Creative children are always solving problems in *new* ways, ways nobody expected. While they may be aware that teachers and principals want them to be orderly, systematic, and consistent, they *know* they are not that way and probably never can be. Creative children and adolescents suffer for their imagination, impulsiveness, and unpredictability in almost every kind of school, where the rewards of good marks and honors go to those who display the Boy Scout virtues. Most teachers cannot cope with the highly original child. And with originality and inventiveness usually goes resistance to submission. A creative sixteen-year-old boy I know finds it irresistible to exit from his science class by the fire-escape ladder which is:

1. Fun.
2. Dramatic.
3. Attention-getting.
4. Athletically satisfying.

When asked why he continues to do this, he could only imitate the climber of Everest, who replied, "Because it is there!" He was informed by the assistant principal that exiting by the fire escape is also:

1. Against the rules.
2. Possibly dangerous.

He continued to use the ladder, was suspended from school, and will be seeking a different school next year. One could ask, "Why couldn't he just use the stairs like everybody else?" To the highly creative adolescent who feels trapped in a conventional or rigid school, doing *anything* like everybody else soon becomes unbearably irritating. For him, doing something unconventional becomes necessary, to show him he is still himself. I think this is one of the underlying reasons why on many high school and college campuses, the leading rebels and demonstrators seem to be highly creative and unconventional adolescents who have been starved for a setting in which they could be themselves. They find, at last, in student revolts a way to express some originality, to get some action, to make something *happen* that is not orderly and utterly boring. ("Strike because your classes are a bore. . . . Strike because they are squeezing the life out of you!") Edgar Z. Friedenberg in his book, *Coming of Age in America* revealed starkly how strong are the pressures for conformity in the American high school—public, private, or parochial. Frederick Wiseman's film *High School,* documents the same lamentable fact. If you are a creative, original, nonconforming young person, there is almost no place you can feel at home. You are not going to give up your creativity. You may have seen your parents or their friends give up the development of their talents in art, music, or theatre in favor of business or homemaking, but that fills you with despair. To you they are sellouts. You need to learn how you can live a creative life, make society accept it somehow. If you are really creative, you would much rather give up society than give up your creative style. You hunger to see how others have made it; you need examples.

Thus a necessary part of psychotherapy for creative adolescents is *an apprenticeship in the creative life.* We have provided that in our program through our teachers. Somewhat in the way that Maslow described, we pay attention to neurosis and defenses in individual and group therapy and we pay attention to potential and creative growth in the creative classes and apprenticeships. Remove the barriers, let the feelings and ideas flow out, teach the adolescent techniques for expression and for channeling his creative ideas, and show him examples of how others have done it before him.

A very creative friend of mine told me of a scheme once proposed for a new and better way of dealing with adolescents. According to his plan, the government would subsidize young people for awhile so they could go anywhere and try learning how to do interesting things before they chose a definite occupation. The basic idea was that young people should not have to do what they don't want to do, that they should do what turns them on, and that that takes finding. Laughing, my friend and I devised the title, the Self Corps, for this new organization which of course will never get off the drawing-board. But the goal is right: Find out what turns you on, then—find a way to do it. And creative kids who are not turned on by academic schooling and "straight" jobs need to become strong enough to find creative apprenticeships doing whatever they love to do.

Recently David brought Taj Mahal, a famous blues musician, to the blues class with him. For four hours the students, Dave and Taj sat together making beautiful and soulful blues. At one point Taj began telling the kids how the blues felt for him, how he made the blues his life. What he was revealing was his wholeness: he had made his life out of what he loved. Afterward a young drummer said, "I learned more about music this afternoon than all the years I've been playing." And almost every other young musician who had been there told me, each in his own way, that this had been a great day in their lives. They need to know how an adult lives a creative life. They found out that afternoon how one man felt in his center.

When I write about the classes at the School, the reader must conceive of our situation as quite different from that of almost any school he has ever attended or heard about. The factors that seem to underlie these special relationships the students and teachers form with each other at the School are:

> Teachers are selected because they are working for self-actualization in their creative lives. They spend their lives doing what they most care about.
> Our students are aware of self-actualization and are trying to find it in their own lives.
> Teachers can thus recognize and empathize with this search in their students.

Thus students feel the teachers' interest and can relate to them as sharers of a common path and goal.

Bill put it more succinctly in describing his relationship with David: "As soon as I could see what his trip was, I wanted to make my own trip like his. He does whatever he has to do in order to be freer and more fully creative as a musician."

What takes place in the other classes at the School? Some of our classes stress individual development and some work as a group. If you visit an arts class you see a boy welding together a steel sculpture, a girl making a wire mobile, three students drawing from a model, two others building a rather abstract wooden house for a cat and painting it purple and orange. In a corner a girl paints on a small piece of glass and covers it with another piece. There are two teachers. Dick travels from one student to the next giving advice, commenting, answering questions. Dick's style of teaching mirrors his way of conducting his own life and his view of how an artist develops. When I first asked him for a description of the goals of his class, he said "I'll take them up to the edge of pure space, and then they're on their own. I want to help each student take his own trip, wherever he wants to go in art—from building a box that encloses space all the way to oil painting." Dick has done just that. For the first session or two, he started with building and understanding boxes—"because we are working in art with space, and a box is the most obvious container to hold space, right? And there are a lot of trips in a box to interest someone. The inside is a vessel, and the outside is a surface. And the joints in a corner point in three directions. Students can get interested in all kinds of things about a box, and take it from there!" And they did. Then after two sessions boxes were transformed. The journey for the kids in Dick's class was from the security of a container on which everyone worked together, to a solo flight in painting or welding. As a metal sculptor, I taught the technique of welding to five of Dick's students and watched them move more and more freely into self-expression in steel and brass.

Later we found Carol to teach along with Dick. Like Dick, painting is Carol's life. Between them they are able to reach just about every student in the class. Having two teachers with very different personalities works well because it allows each teacher to proceed in his own way, to be himself or herself just as much as we are encouraging the kids to be themselves. What we are teaching is how to be *yourself* in a creative project, not how to produce art works. So the atmosphere permits everyone in the room, teachers and students, to do what they want to do, so long as it involves art. Records are always playing loudly, mostly rock and blues. Kids bring their friends to the class as guests, but no one watches—everyone participates. Last Saturday I met a neighbor of mine in the art class, drawing a portrait, and a young girl introduced herself. She had been driving along the highway and picked up a hitchhiker who turned out to be one of our art students. She ended up taking the class with him and left us a couple of nice drawings when she took off.

There is an obvious relationship between the greater freedom the students show in their art work and the greater freedom of emotional expression they learn from group and individual therapy. For example, Alice has been coming to Dick's class for about two months and seeing me individually as well. At about the same time as I was helping Alice to see how dependent she is on others and how she clings to people, she began making pictures in the art class which showed less constraint and more freedom. And one day she showed me one of her pictures. "This one I did without any help from anyone! It's really mine!" And that is the one we hung up in the art studio. At the same time as she began producing independent art Alice began living more independently as well and for the first time enjoyed being on her own.

The dance-drama class began quite differently from the

visual arts class. It started as two separate classes—a dance class taught by Lois and a drama class taught by June. At first we had few students. Both classes limped along with two or three students each for several weeks. Both teachers were distressed. Students felt too self-conscious working in such small groups. The kids were inhibited, didn't want to appear foolish. The School was new, and they didn't know each other well enough yet to dare expose themselves to each other. At this early point in our development they had not yet revealed much in the group therapy sessions either. The atmosphere was tense with the fear of "being put down if people find out what you are like."

Then Lois and June combined their classes. And we accumulated more students; now the class had ten or twelve regular members. The kids had become more used to the group therapy situation they also shared, and they felt safer now with one another. Almost from the first combined session, the dance-drama class became exciting and alive. Improvisation became freer and the students came to trust each other much more. I began attending as many of the classes as I could, because I found I could learn so much more about the kids from watching how they created dramatic improvisations and used their bodies to solve movement problems.

June and Lois have each put into words what goes on in their classes. June describes her work in this way:

"In teaching drama at the School, I find that I am somewhere between teaching specific skills on the one hand and doing therapy on the other. Although I use the same sort of materials for my classes at the School as I do with the classes I teach elsewhere, there is a difference in my approach, one that is hard to describe accurately.

"For one thing, I am less concerned with the final product than in other teaching situations. I am far more concerned with the process. I find myself stressing exercises and improvisations that will lead toward better group rapport among the participating students. In fact, getting the group to work together as a creative unit is, I think, primary goal for the class. And because of the personality problems of some members of the class, this is often a long-term and heavy task.

"In order to get the group to function as a creative unit, I have to be acutely aware of individual difficulties and needs. For example, if Gary or Louis were in an especially disturbed mood and either one or both of them were in class, then I would have to deal very directly with their problems before the class could function at all. This might mean inventing new exercises of themes for improvs right on the spot—based on some intuition as to what would help them, that particular afternoon. When especially difficult situations arise, there is no time to think and plan. In that respect I feel that my abilities as a performer, my own skill at improvising, is especially useful. In a sense I have to improvise along with them, in order to guide them out of whatever funk or depression or anger they are in at the moment, in order to unite them with the rest of the students. Very often I have to alter my plans for the afternoon, or drop them entirely. Because of my own particular personality make-up I do not find this in any way disturbing, although it was disturbing when I first began teaching at the School. At first I had some preconceived idea about what a teacher's duty was—that I had to be sure the kids learned all the things I thought they ought to learn, things I knew they would need in order to be able to learn how to improvise dramatically. At this point, I have very few such preconceptions left. I swing with it and throw in a thing or two of my own when people are in a relaxed mood and thus able to swing with me. I arrive in class with four times as many ideas as we will have time for, and therefore able to switch very readily, or—if it seems necessary—abandon my whole program and dream up something new on the spot. These new ideas on the spot come from the students themselves. By that I mean that I observe very closely what they are doing and saying and use that material to stimulate my own creative ideas. That is why I find my teaching at the School exciting. I am continually challenged and continually organically involved with the process at the moment. Teaching that class is one of the most immediate *present* things I do. Although I say that I use intuition in making instant decisions to pursue a course other than the one I planned, this intuition is actually based upon years of experience teaching improvised drama. I feel now I have an encyclopedia of material I carry around in my head—available to me when I need it.

"One of the most common problems that arises in class is that of the release and handling of aggression. Over the years of teaching it has become obvious to me that many group improvs lead directly to aggressive behavior—especially when we use masks. This is true with all age groups, with all racial and cultural backgrounds. Rather than avoid those particular exercises that provoke aggression, I have taken another tack, that I find both helpful to those participating and artistically useful. In setting up the format or skeleton for an improvisation, I allow for aggressive behavior to unfold and then help the students to understand that once people start hitting each other or killing each other (in intent, not actuality—though sometimes people get carried away and I have to stop the action) the play is bound to end. "Once you're dead, you're dead," I tell them. Short of a resurrection miracle you can't get back up again and enter the improv. So the trick of it is to sustain the tension and prolong the action, to put off the aggressive acts until they become more potent dramatically. In other words, I try to teach them how to control their aggression both individually and as a group so that they will be able to use it when they choose to do so. They learn to use aggression to further the plot or action and in the long run, as a force in the creation of a group play.

"Other problems that arise are the opposite: shy people who need help in being more forward and less retiring. Arlene was once so shy and withdrawn that I could hardly hear her speak. She is currently taking a much more active role in the plays. I purposely create and structure situations that will allow the withdrawn students to express themselves within a fairly safe context at first. Then gradually I help them find situations which are more challenging. In general I try to guide them from just where they are at that moment into a more positive, more creative next place. I have few preconceptions as to where the next place may be for each student, and I am constantly amazed and excited by the leaps people take in new directions.

"Some students—Louisa is one currently—are highly original and unique in everything they do. In class I feel humble before these gifts and don't want to rob or destroy the original impulses in students like Louisa. But often the impulses are entirely out of key with what everyone else is doing, and thus destructive to group improvs. Usually this is because Louisa, or whoever it is at the moment, is so intent on their own little plot or plan that they have failed to be sensitive to what everyone else is into. In discussing what has happened during the class, I try to point out this dilemma. I often say things like, 'That was a superb and original idea, but you pulled it too soon—before the others were ready to accept it,' or, 'You were in your own little play and not in the play the others were creating,' or, 'You have a special talent to create plot, and that won't disappear. We'll need that skill later on, but for now concentrate more on getting connected with the other people.'

"It's a remarkable thing about improvs, that they are always more than the sum of their parts, that when everyone is functioning together as a creative unit, no one has to sacrifice his own uniqueness or give up individual creative powers. Just the contrary. Each individual in the improv is brought out of himself on the one hand and into high gear creatively on the other. This experience, when it works, is so exhilarating to the participants that it seems to give them a real high, a feeling of personal satisfaction and warmth and affection for the other people in the group.

"One of the things I continually watch for is a repeated pattern of behavior in the improvs. That is, sometimes a person will play the same role over and over. Usually it is because there is in that role something of deep personal concern to that student. Sally, for instance, always played aggressive roles. Some time ago Artie always played the in-between man who got people together. My experience has been that I help the student in such a situation to *perfect* that particular role, master it so to speak, shape it artistically. Then, when this is accomplished, I tell them, 'Well, you've really come to grips with that role. Do you realize how often you play it? I think it's time to expand your vocabulary.' Sometimes when this occurs there is protest on the part of the student because taking on new roles and expanding new emotional vocabularies requires taking a bigger risk. I urge them on to this new endeavor by saying, 'I can't believe that you're so limited, that you don't have thousands of characters and ideas in you.' And I'm always right about that. People vastly underestimate their own potential, even those students who seem to be so sure of themselves, like Sally.

"Now that I teach the class together with Lois, time does not allow as much discussion over what has happened, as when I held a drama class on my own. But, for beginners, I have come to feel that the raw experience of it all is much more important than discussions. Doing lots of new things without too much time to think and ponder whether it's being done correctly or poorly is good for the beginner.

"I try to reassure students that they do not have to judge or censor themselves during the improvs, that I'm there to stop things if they get out of hand, to be the eye and the critic. This relieves them of the burden of trying to do and to criticize at the same time. Little by little, however, I try to get them to criticize each other with a commonly acquired vocabulary that we develop and share together, because big leaps in skill occur when you can be critical about your own work. Commenting on each other's work not only leads the student to self-awareness, it is also an exercise in how to help others in a constructive manner. I always insist that the criticism of each other start from where the person is, not where you the critic are. You talk about what they've done, not what you wish they'd do or what you think they ought to have done.

"In assuming the role of the critic and the eye, I have consciously opted out of the personality-cult type of teaching. Every once in awhile this gives me a selfish little pang. I often have to make a choice between becoming somebody's buddy, someone whom I very much like, or staying just that little bit detached, objective, to guide them instead. At times, through the whole atmosphere of the School I find myself becoming especially attached to a few particular students. This was a great problem to me during my first year of teaching at the School, but because of my own heavy involvement with my family and with other teaching commitments as well as my professional acting and directing, I've decided to limit personal involvement with students outside of School hours. Occasionally I feel sad about this and wish my life style were a bit more leisurely, more able to include students coming and going in and out of my home. This applies to my feelings about fellow staff members as well. I enjoy most of the staff personally, and would very much like to get to know some of them better, spend more time with them socially. On the other hand teaching at the School has deeply influenced my teaching in general and my personal life specifically. I find myself less patient with the ordinary subterfuges of personal relationships. I find myself much more willing to be open and truthful with other people than most people either want to be or find it comfortable to be. This has always been true of me. But the School has intensified this aspect of my personality. Little by little I am cutting myself loose from situations in which there is no interchange of feelings, and in that way I am a bit lonelier on the one hand, but more content with those relationships I retain, on the other.

"In regard to my own family—my husband and my daughters—I find myself better able to deal with problems that arise than I had been before. And in many respects I feel that the atmosphere at the School has helped me. There is no question but what I am able to deal with the problems of my teen-age daughters as a result of my experiences at the School. Things which would have panicked me do not do so now. My daughter's need for independence is not a threat to me, despite the fact that her choices are not always what I would have chosen for her. I have been able to guide her through periods of drug involvement in a way that helped her, and she has come out on the other side of it wiser and really more 'together.' My experience at the School has been very helpful to my friends as well. Various friends with teen-age kids have turned to me for advice and I find that I have been able to reassure them and help them work their way through crises without panic. That is the chief bugaboo—panic and resulting irrational decisions—to clamp down on their kids, to punish them, instead of helping them to free themselves so they can do what they need or want to do.

"I find it's essential to me to be involved in personally creative activity in addition to the School, to be acting and directing myself, and that it helps to inspire and reinforce me. I find that in the end my students benefit from the kind of energy my creative life gives me. I notice that when I have had long periods of only teaching, I tend to be soggier, less alert, more mundane in my classes, than when I am actively involved in the theater myself. Recently I've been writing fiction a lot, and that is feeding into my classes. I'm more able to help students develop plot and the writing aspect of improvs, because I'm more aware of the function of language and the architectural structuring of the material we're working on. This has given me courage to set out on our current venture: the creation of a show about people at the School and about the School.

"A final word about my own personal association with the School. Working with Lois—sharing the classes—is a very rewarding experience to me. Lois's personal point of view is often an inspiration, an added dimension to my own or a very different input. When I get stale, I look to her for new thoughts and directions and feel that this is true the other way round as well. Also, the serious and fun and reassuring influence of Shep in the School makes working there part of my total life experience rather than a 'job.' I have always had the feeling that although we may disagree, the leadership of the School is always sensitive to my own personal requests or difficulties, and that somehow, somewhere, solutions to most problems will be found. I look forward to School days, no matter what else is going on in my life!"

Lois, who has taught at the School since it began, describes her teaching experiences in these words:

"The dance class has gone through many changes: at first I tried to make it a straight technique class similar to ones I've had myself, because this way you can train a body to move better. But there were obvious problems: not enough students, very self-conscious students, shaky motivation for making that kind of self-exposure and change, and a huge discrepancy in skill levels. Adding improvisational problems and sensitivity exercises to the class helped students, but not me. I still had big unanswered questions in my head. What was I doing? What were my goals? What could I realistically expect, and how to get it? Was it dance? Was it dance therapy? But I didn't want to be a dance therapist; I wanted people to get excited about dance, to find pleasure in moving, alone and together, and to be willing to accept some discipline toward that goal.

"Combining with June's drama class was a big help. It made a better size class for both of us, and gradually a format evolved which still works. There are five parts to the class which June and I discuss and plan together and share the leadership of. I do the movement, she does the drama, and in each class there's some natural alternation of how these go together, based on what they are, the problems of themes we're working on that day, or how one relates to or evolves into another. We mainly comment and give criticism on the part we each have taught. Although there are frequent overlapping comments that apply to both dance and drama, specific skill criticisms are given by one or the other of us, not both. We respect each other's performing and teaching skill and thus sharing has never been a problem for June and me. Here's a typical class plan:

> WARM-UP: Back slapping in pairs.
> TECHNIQUE: Work on heads, shoulders (exercises), *pliés* in first and second positions, something for the feet, especially metatarsals, work on beginning turns.
> ACROSS THE FLOOR: Simple walk with arms—then turns, triplets, plain and with turns.
> PROBLEMS: Trios: Make a phrase that locomotes, know the counts, teach it to the class, and perform it all together.
> Duets or Trios: Improvise, choosing one prop (Chinese jump-ropes, blanket, chair, box). Do it in silence and then repeat using music. Perform it for the class.
> COOL OFF: Group lifts in threes, catching and falling to a breath rhythm.

"In the PROBLEMS section, June also plans acting problems. We always plan much more than we use. We never get to a lot of things because something always catches on and needs time to develop. But I always keep lots in my head to choose from. Sometimes as we sit on the sidelines and watch, a new and much better idea comes to us on the spot, and we do that instead of the 'class plan.'

"I taught the dance class separately from September, 1968, till March, 1969. We then combined and June and I have been together ever since. But soon I felt that there were a few students emerging who again needed the challenge of a pure dance class, so I started a separate intermediate-level dance class on Saturdays, while continuing the (beginning-level) dance-drama class with June on Wednesdays. Eventually I gave the Saturday class over to Mari, who's a fine dancer and a very experienced teacher. Another interesting need emerged out of the wedding of Bob and Ildri, our psychodrama leaders. The School put together and performed a 'wedding masque' as a gift to them, and the experience of collaborating with writers, musicians, painters, and everybody in the School to make the 'performance' at their wedding was so exciting we wanted to continue it in some way, to give the classes a performing goal. So June and I started a new kind of class on Friday afternoons. Or rather, we auditioned all students interested in performing, and we picked five (three girls, two boys), the number we wanted to work with. These rehearsals are like an advanced section of the drama-dance class. We intend to keep the basic number at five, but to collaborate with others in the School as we need them. One boy has offered to build a set for our show, another to help with writing a script, etc.

"The Friday class, called 'Identity, Inc.' rehearsal, has evolved its own plan, suggested partly by June and me, partly by the kids. We have:

A BEGINNING RITUAL (The same each week): The purpose of this is to get them reacquainted with their bodies, voices, each other. It's a "tune-up" for projection.

MOVEMENT WARM-UP

ACTING WARM-UP: Students take turns being responsible for leading the movement and acting warm-ups.

ACTING PROBLEMS: The theme so far has been "Collision." Improvisations are tried, criticized, analyzed, repeated.

COOL-OFF RITUAL: Students get quiet together.

"One week there was a 'collision improvisation' which proved to be a fine example of creative teaching and learning. Arlene was absent, so we had an even number of students (not the usual five). We decided to use this accident of being two pairs, and set up boy-girl relationship problems as the collision improv for the day. They were to start with one doing something physical—a gesture, a movement, to set the scene; the other would enter, react to the feeling, and the dialogue would proceed from there. Ann began by walking, sort of bouncing around, happily hugging herself. Marty entered and she threw her arms around him and hugged him, saying: 'Hey, I'm glad to see you!' Marty answered, 'Wow, you're feeling horny today!' Ann tried to defend her mood, but it became obvious that she was thrown by Marty's reaction and the improv began to founder. Ann stopped it, started to help others analyze how things had gotten derailed, when she suddenly burst into real tears and said she couldn't do it, didn't want to continue, that this kind of misinterpretation of her feelings was what was always happening to her in her own life. June now insisted that Ann try again and that she *use* her real distress about the misunderstanding to make the improv work. The key to the success of it was in going *with* the real feelings, not denying them. If Marty felt confused or defensive about Ann's coming on so strong, he would have to show it, and Ann in turn would have to express her anger or disappointment with him, if the dialogue were to have any integrity. They did repeat it once more. Ann brought her feelings under control and she did a beautiful job. The whole class applauded. This particular problem also illustrates something else that we had all discussed and agreed upon. None of us wanted the improvisations to be "acting out being at the School," and yet how could we make them 'real,' related both to the students' feelings and to the life of the School? How could we evolve a 'script' that would be personal but not embarrassingly autobiographical? I think we've found the right direction. The key is the theme. If the themes are right, they relate to real feelings, which makes the dialogue emotionally true, and therefore theatrically valid.

"We've gotten a small grant with which we'll buy some used videotape equipment so that improvs can be taped, reviewed, discarded, or kept for development. At some point a writer or writers will collaborate with us on polishing this 'found' material."

Lois and June have put into words the kinds of considerations going on in the minds of all the teachers at the School. A balance of structure and freedom, a long-range goal for the class combined with constant sensitivity to the immediate feelings and needs of the particular students in the class— these are the challenges facing each one of our teachers. A good example came up recently, described by June:

"A revealing incident occurred in the dance-drama workshop. The problem with which people were working for the afternoon was that of scenes with a psychiatrist and a patient. We had tried such scenes in the performing group and found them almost impossible to do. It became clear that the role of the psychiatrist was very difficult, nearly impossible for them to portray because of the special knowledge and technique required.

"In this particular improv Louisa played the patient and Markie the doctor. Louisa began her complaints by saying she had a problem about our dance-drama class, that she hated the class because the teachers made her make a fool of herself. She went on to describe how arrogant she felt in the class and said she hated herself for her arrogance. Then she got into talking about how much she hates her mother, how afraid she is that some day she'll kill her mother.

"It isn't Lois's and my usual style to go into the content of the personal problems revealed in the class, unless the matter simply cries out to be discussed, and we felt this certainly did. I asked everyone to sit down near us, which they did, and then I asked Louisa how much of what she had said was for dramatic effect, and how much she really meant. Was she using the opportunity to express her own personal, long-term fears and resentments? She said that these were true feelings, that she felt we in the class were inducing her to make a fool of herself. I then explained to her that I did not feel that she had ever made a fool of herself, and Lois agreed. The truth of the matter was, I said, that the worst thing about her work was that she tended to do things halfway, never taking the biggest risk of looking foolish or being wrong; I felt she was so overconcerned about seeming foolish that she defended herself by saying inwardly, 'What they are doing in this class is idiotic, and I won't be part of it,' therefore she came out looking arrogant, and hated herself for it. Louisa began to realize now what a vicious circle she was in, and Lois and I added more examples of what we meant, so she'd understand. Still we reassured her that we would not allow her to make a fool of herself, that we wouldn't allow anyone in the class to do that, that we are there to prevent that from happening, to protect everyone from that.

"In the meantime, Deborah began to identify with Louisa's conflict, saying she too often felt she was making a fool of herself. I pointed out to her that her problem seemed to me very different from Louisa's, that in fact she was able to throw herself into the improvisations with great abandon and freedom, that what troubled her was perhaps the feeling she was a showoff, or narcissistic; maybe someone had told her sometime that she was a showoff. She agreed readily, recalling that her family had always made her feel that this kind of enthusiastic self-expression was 'not nice'.

"Now we went on to discuss the question of throwing your self into your work in the performing arts, both dance and acting—committing yourself and feeling you have a right to enjoy it. I felt that this discussion was fruitful to everyone, that the other members of the class listened and were deeply interested; you could just see them applying bits of the conversation to their own problems.

"At the end of the class Lois suggested we turn off the lights and stand in a tight circle, just hold each other and sway together. This was very helpful in changing the feeling of tension to one of feeling good about each other. People came over and sat down near me afterward and continued our discussion in low and intimate tones. Louisa talked with me a bit more now about her problems in art school, where she feels no one ever gives her any response, as if they don't notice her or her work. This was such a categorical statement that I came away feeling that Lois and I must help Louisa to learn how to *ask* for feedback about her work, and also to become a little tougher, more able to take creative chances. Also, Lois said she intends to help Louisa learn how to value herself more as a beautiful young woman, how in particular to value her body more.

"It seems to me with Louisa that because of her terrible relationship to her mother, which she told us about in group therapy, she has simply missed having a decent woman with whom she can identify, someone she can admire. She is thus suspicious of other women, and it is vital for her to learn to make decent relationships with women even before she can do it with men. At least that's my instinct about her. I'm hoping I can extend myself personally more to Louisa, because I've come to understand more of what she feels. I've found it hard so far to make deep contact with her other than fleetingly. Also, I think the ice is broken now between us because I accepted her hostile feelings about the class and tried to understand their source, instead of simply becoming defensive and putting her down for them.

"As far as Deborah is concerned, I feel I should reassure her that when she does throw herself into something, it's great. She has such verve, vitality and energy and an ability to put that energy into creative activity, but she needs encouragement to value this ability.

"Lois and I, in discussions since that class, have decided that we will leave more time for discussion and cool-off at the end of each class, that we'll spend more time now and then on the 'therapy aspects' of the class. We are sometimes so eager to 'get on with the show' that we pass over opportunities to use the class therapeutically. We do this, I should add, only when we feel we can understand what's going on and when we feel we can cope with it. This is not always true; then we leave the problem alone and let it be dealt with in group therapy."

It is an enormous advantage to the kids to have Lois and June as teachers, an advantage both creatively and therapeutically, though the class is not conceived nor conducted as "drama therapy." Lois and June have never quit being in the center ring in their creative lives. Lois started in college as a dance student and went to New York from the midwest at twenty-one to study modern dance at Martha Graham's studio. When she got married after two years there and started having kids, she felt a profound lack in her life—a gulf that was not filled by having a husband and four children. She went on taking dance classes between pregnancies, and finally at age thirty-nine, she had her first professional performance. From the "oldest intermediate dance student" she knew, she was transformed into the "oldest new performer." She performed actively for seven years in two dance companies. Now she has retired from active performing because she feels she no longer can maintain the technical proficiency for difficult movement, and has begun working on becoming a choreographer. She remains the administrative director of a dance company and is working on dance ideas of her own, trying them out on the young dancers in that company. It's clear that she is never going to quit, never going to diminish her involvement with dance and theatre. She is not like a more often encountered kind of "art teacher" found in schools everywhere, someone who allowed marriage and child-raising to substitute for a creative career, and then turned to teaching, an admission that she never was or no longer considers herself an artist. Lois's standard for her choreography are as rigorous as they were for her dancing. The work must be first-rate.

June is also in her forties, married, with two kids. She could have gone into teaching or some other creatively less demanding work any time, and she would have been home every evening and out of the frenzy and anxiety of first nights. But since she started acting professionally about ten years ago, she has kept on trying out for roles, kept on learning parts, kept on appearing on the stage and television. Her husband, who is a successful management consultant and himself a composer, has given her as much flak from time to time about all this as I have given Lois, but neither of them have even dreamed seriously of quitting, and both husbands are proud of them. I know that in my case, I consider Lois's dance career gives her so much sparkle and energy, so much creative vitality, that her whole bearing and state of being is enhanced by that involvement. As frustrated as I become when rehearsals get to be every night for weeks before a performance, I've learned that it's worth it for her and thus for me and our sons.

The fact that Lois and June are active professionals in dance and theatre makes them apply the lessons of real performance and real production to the issues that come up in the classes they teach at the School. So many kids have said about the teachers in the high schools and prep schools and colleges they attend, that they are not *really* "into anything but teaching." They respect someone who really *does* the skill he teaches. And this gives the teacher prestige as an identification figure, and enhances a creative apprenticeship, as we have seen with Bill and David, and for many other kids at the School with their teachers.

Another enormous advantage our teachers have at the School is that they are in "training" not as therapists, but as teachers who become aware, through week-by-week involvement in a therapy group with their students, of the problems and blocks which paralyze kids seeking freedom of creative expression. In Maslow's words, "Only the one who respects fear and defense can teach; only the one who respects health can do therapy." The School trains teachers by making them aware of fear and defense in their students, and it trains therapists by reminding them what health is. The young psychiatrist who assists me at the School told me the other night, "I'm so happy with my therapy group here. The atmosphere of the School got me feeling so much freer and less afraid, that I can take chances with my group here, and it pays off! The group gets deeper and closer than the ones I run anywhere else!" These points cannot be overemphasized, I believe. They describe the atmosphere of the School, and atmosphere is an intangible; but it's the atmosphere that makes kids get well. We don't have to cope with the absurd situation that exists in most "mental health centers" and clinics, where unrealized people in unhealthy environments train other people to do therapy. In those settings you lose respect for health because it has been years since you encountered it. In a place where the personnel office, the treasurer, the Civil Service, the pay scale, the work conditions, the atmosphere, are ungratifying, the therapist himself feels uncared for and frustrated; this attitude must and does affect his work.

Creative people who do creative work are much more in touch with how they feel. Emotionally disturbed people are almost always out of touch with how they feel. One of the central dynamics of the therapeutic community at the School is the development of intimacy between emotionally disturbed young people and creative older people. The identification which follows is doubly useful, because it teaches the kids two lessons at once:

1. You *can* get your head together.
2. A creative life, based on self-actualization, *is* possible.

# 8 › Group Therapy: Finding Openness

CHRIS AND WANDA and the other adolescents and young adults we work with need to learn much more than creative skills like painting or acting. There are already plenty of painters and actors who like many businessmen and professionals have low self-esteem and have trouble making honest, loving relationships, with other people. Why not, I thought, combine training in the arts and other skills with personal therapy, but in a new way? Why not train teachers and students together through group therapy—train them to be open with each other? When I came across Maslow's comments about education and therapy (quoted earlier), I realized how our model puts such ideas into action. On the one hand, our teachers are free to teach painting, acting, guitar, dance, filmmaking, *without* attempting to become "art therapists." They do not try to *interpret* the "meaning" of a painting or an improvisation. They simply start teaching each student at the point of artistic development where they find him and help him go further along the path of developing his talent. And in our program, as in all good art education, comparisons, expectations, and efforts to induce conformity are at a minimum; helping the student express more skillfully his *own* visions and messages is the goal. On the other hand, as Maslow suggests, if a teacher is *aware* of doubts, fears, immaturities and held-in feelings in his students, he teaches with deeper understanding. Not a therapist, he still appreciates how the problems of his student hold him back, make him less free. The teacher who *knows* his student deeply teaches him more *personally*. And in an age when personal involvement of older people with young people is so hard to find, this is absolutely vital. For this reason, we decided that all students and teachers in the School We Have should see one another each week in a group therapy session. When the School got larger, we divided the sessions into two groups, then four groups. Teachers attend groups just as students do.

A most important value of the group sessions has been helping the kids get to know their teachers in depth. Remember the cries from the kids whose stories I told earlier. "Never close to my parents," "teachers who just do it for the paycheck," "they don't know me and I don't know them!"—this is the cry of the alienated adolescent. Kids of this age are really interested in how older people make a life for themselves. What is important? What do artists, writers, dancers feel and what must they contend with? How do marriage and raising a family fit in? The effect of old and young honestly sharing their deeper feelings is electrifying. In Erikson's terms, it creates the kind of atmosphere in which identity formation is made easier, in which a young person can compare himself to an older one and perhaps say, "I want to be like him!" At the School we are a living embodiment of Mead's cocognitive culture: we are learning from each other. Everyone is talking about the "generation gap." At our School we do something about it.

My years at the School have broken down my old views about the traditional facade of the therapist. Over and over again, when I have revealed my own past or present problems most honestly, the response from the group has been an opening-up. Not only do I get new understanding from revealing myself to the group of adolescents and nonprofessional adults, but I often come away from a group session feeling as much new insight as I ever did from my individual sessions with any one of my three analysts. My own revelations and those of other staff members do not hurt our roles as therapists and teachers. On the contrary, our positions are helped, because we are more real to the kids. Often I have heard the kids express the feelings, "If you have problems like mine, and you made it as far as you did, I guess I can too. I wish my parents would talk to me as openly as you have!"

A couple of years ago I went to an "encounter center" in California for an encounter group week. Here I learned what it was like to be a member of a group when the leader would *not* reveal his own feelings. Well-trained, intelligent, and in command of a situation, wearing love beads and long hair, this new-age guru played as clever a game of facade-maintenance as ever a psychoanalyst could. Direct appeals for his feelings, his opinions, were met with silence. Over and over again he advised group members to reveal "how you feel right now about what is going on," but could not or would not do the same himself. One evening when an emergency arose in his life, he could not come to the meeting and the mood was just like that of a high school class when the math teacher doesn't show up. We got high on wine, made up dirty songs about the "human potential movement," and some of us at least came away feeling this was the best session of the entire week. When the therapist and the adult staff members reveal themselves, it helps the group, it is therapeutic. When the staff members hold back, it creates a "we-they" situation, all too familiar from home and high school, and less progress is made. If the goal is to face problems, open them up and deal with them, then let us see adults doing it, just as they advise the kids to do it. The rightness of this point of view has been underlined ever since we started psychodrama groups at the School. Several of those making the greatest progress toward emotional openness and freedom have been staff members.

Of course, there are only so many hours of group therapy time per week, and three times as many kids as staff, so I advise some selection by the group leaders lest the sessions become dominated by the staff members' problems. In my groups I give preference to those problems that involve the School or people at the School, whether the person who brings them up is student or staff. If no one has an issue of mutual relevance, then anyone can bring up his problems with his life outside the School. Lately, we have changed our Wednesday evenings format for "group night." We start with supper for all, then a School group meeting, then we split up for two to three hours more of small group (twelve to fifteen members) therapy. I am trying to get issues of importance to all of us brought up in the whole School group meeting, so more personal concerns can be aired in the small groups afterwards.

The idea of everyone being open has resulted in great and obvious changes in a lot of us at the School, changes toward freedom of expression and self-acceptance. About as much improvement has occurred in the staff as in the students. Aside from the personal benefits, we end up with better teachers.

The question of confidentiality arises, but it has been easily solved. When I feel that some information I have about a student or staff member is relevant to what they are saying in the group, I simply ask his permission then and there to introduce it. "Al, can I talk about some of your hassles with your father that you told me about?" Usually he agrees. If not, I do not introduce it. The openness of our groups is such that there is almost nothing that one cannot say, once having asked permission.

As we have come to know each other better, the group sessions have focused much more on people's emotional problems and much less on rule-making and community policy. The group has become loving and therapeutic. It does not exert the relentless pressure for expression of feelings that you find in many adult groups. But the group has become intimate and honest. We trust each other now, and we reveal how we feel about each other and our own lives. The group accepts cries for help and concern, revelations of anger and competitiveness, the whole gamut of honest human feelings.

An episode from one of our sessions involving a student named Arthur makes a fine example:

Arthur has been getting into trouble. He bought a motorcycle with borrowed money. He was contemplating paying back his creditors with money he could make by selling drugs. His parents knew nothing of all these maneuvers. Now the creditors were demanding money and Arthur was under pressure.

*Arthur*: "I don't know why I do these things. I knew I had to have a motorcycle, then when I got one it was too small, not impressive enough. So I traded it for a really big one. And I can't pay for it. Now I got a ticket for not having it registered. I'm worried my parents will find out."

*Group Member*: "Arthur, why didn't you wait until you got old enough for a motorcycle license and till you saved up the money to buy one? Why did you have to do it so fast?"

*Arthur*: "It was just after my girl started to like another guy and stopped caring about me. I was depressed."

*Another Group Member*: "So maybe you needed to build yourself up again. The motorcycle is great, but maybe it was really an ego trip, to make up for being shot down by a chick!"

*Arthur*: "I always worry that girls will put me down—when they get to know me, they'll prefer some other guy. I'm always telling them I'm older, trying to impress them."

*Group Member*: "Arthur, why do you feel so sure no one will like you? You're a nice guy, a good musician—"

*Arthur*: "Well, I always had to please my older sister—she was really terrible to me. For years, she picked on me, made me give her things and do things for her. Really cut me down. And I couldn't tell my parents about what she was doing, either, or she would really give me hell. I always had to please her. Now I think of girls as if they were like her. They'll put me down.

"And I can't risk hurting my parents by telling them anything I did that might upset them. They had such trouble with my sister that I felt I should give them nothing but happiness. Arthur couldn't have problems!"

The group members, like Arthur, are sixteen years old on the average. And they have plenty of problems of their own at home, at school, and inside themselves. But they were able to show Arthur a few vital things about Arthur:

1. That he labors against feelings of inferiority, probably dating back to years of enslavement to his disturbed sister.
2. That he tries to compensate for feeling inferior by impressing people (girls and himself) with big motorcycles, posing as a twenty-year-old, and so on.
3. That he is really likable and the group members like him.
4. That he doesn't *need* to impress people and appear to be the perfect son.

Shortly after this group session, Arthur revealed his problems to his parents. He told them too that he didn't want to continue in prep school, where he is failing, but to study music on his own. The point is not that the group helped Arthur to become a good student or to live out his father's dreams that he go to college. The group helped Arthur with something much more fundamental: it helped him feel strong enough to reveal his feelings to his parents, to reveal himself to his peers more honestly, to give up the game of impressing people in order to overcome inferiority feelings. This game can become lifelong and Arthur at sixteen is getting rid of it.

One day I noticed a curious phenomenon. I had just reminded a group of kids that it was time to go home, after one of our group therapy sessions. It dawned on me that I was having trouble getting these "dropouts" to leave our school. They were talking to each other and their teachers enthusiastically, dancing, playing music. And these were all kids who "could not communicate" with their parents and other adults. Why has there been no "generation gap" in our place?

On another occasion in our group session, Laura broke down and cried. She had always been scolded and rejected at home; she is the black sheep of the family. Now Alice, her only friend at high school (also a member of our group), is attending a different school and is making new friends.

"I love you, Alice," said Laura, "you're all I have. Nobody wants me, and I'm losing you!"

Alice has very similar problems of her own. She suffers at home through many battles with an unhappy mother, separated from her father. Her only sister has run away. She and Laura were inseparable for awhile; they were the ones nobody else liked. They felt like outcasts. Now Alice had found new strength in our group, and she had transferred to a school she really wanted to go to. She was growing stronger and moving out of Laura's orbit.

As Laura wept and told us how lonely she was, members of the group told her how much they care for her, but they also told Laura how her possessiveness makes people back away from her. It was a tremendously moving experience. Laura could feel the love of the group and at the same time they were showing her how she had contributed to her loneliness by clinging so hard. In the middle of it all, Alice crept over to Laura and held her like a baby.

If there is any kind of human involvement that qualifies more highly for the title "therapy" than what happened between Laura, Alice, and our group, I simply don't know what it is. Laura felt the love she needed as she learned how to get closer to people. Alice gave Laura her love without surrendering her new freedom. And the rest of us helped both of them. From this there is no need to drop out.

The group also works wonderfully as a forum to work out problems which arise during classes. One week our dance-drama class was somewhat disorderly. Several members were feeling that kind of teen-age high that makes you talk, move around, and be unable to concentrate. "Inner speed," someone called it. After the class ended, June brought up the question in the group therapy session, "What went wrong with the drama class?" And I heard five of the kids reply "We were messing up the class by being noisy, interrupting, and distracting everybody." The kids who were now being so totally honest, accepting the responsibility for the chaos in the class were two boys who had to be sent home one day six months earlier because they broke our group's rule against tripping on LSD at our place, a girl who had just missed commitment to a girls' correctional institution, and another girl who had predicted when she first came to us that she could "never tell these people how I feel because you can't trust anybody."

And as the discussion led June to see that she had not been honest enough about her own angry feelings when her class became unruly, suddenly I realized that this is what we were all here for; we were at last really being honest with each other. Teachers, students, those labeled "sick" and those called "well," the veterans of Juvenile Court and the former drug-heads. And something Don once said came back to me and made me smile: "It's so sad you have to go underground to be honest!"

Therapy is *experience*. What really goes on in a therapy group is no more describable than religious experience. So I will not attempt to describe more group interactions. I have watched forty-five adolescents (in three therapy groups) learning from each other that it is safe to reveal yourself to others, that others can really help you. A bond of closeness grows up between the kids and teachers, and this bond is the core of the School We Have. Without encountering each other honestly, we would simply be an after-school art school.

I believe that all schools—art schools, music schools, colleges, trade and craft schools—should not only expose their students to musicians, artists, jewelers, anthropologists, historians, writers, and so on, but that classes should be small and intimacy encouraged, not avoided, as it is in most schools today. Too, all these schools should encourage openness between faculty and students; this might well involve special "openness training" for all, encounter groups or sensitivity training to reorient teachers to the awareness that closeness and openness *teach*. Separateness and uninvolvement of faculty with students do not teach; they lead to alienation and finally rebellion of students. As Paul Goodman put it, high school and college demonstrations and revolts are essentially prison riots. And schools should not be prisons.

As for elementary schools, it is clearly impossible to provide enough mathematicians for seven-year-olds to learn math from, or enough writers or social scientists. At this level of education, the teacher's specialty is the ability to motivate children to want to learn. Anyone who can do this is a teacher, anyone who cannot is *not* a teacher, regardless of degrees earned. Openness training is absolutely essential in teachers' colleges, and should be mandatory. Any candidate who cannot become emotionally open through this training should not be allowed to teach children. In the words of one creative educator, "Teachers' college should be the most exciting kind of school, not the dullest, as many are now."

If we want kids to learn, we must offer *ourselves*. We can't teach facts anymore; the facts we must know in order to live are being updated everyday, and world conditions are changing so fast that our only hope is to teach kids to want to learn, to be excited by learning, and to search out the content of the subjects they want to learn about—a content which is always changing, and which no teacher can possibly keep up with. Schools must provide the *context*, and that context should be one of openness, honesty, intimacy. If our experiment at the School We Have has proved anything it is that openness *teaches*.

# 9 › Individual Therapy: To Recover the Wholeness

"WHAT IS IT LIKE to be a doctor? Do you like being a shrink? Would you go into psychiatry again if you were eighteen now? Do you still love your wife after twenty years? Is it good having kids to bring up? How do you go about making sculpture? Are you as interested in sex as I am?" These are all questions my young patients ask me—and they want answers. I have learned to answer them. Most therapists would not.

In America, an adolescent brought to a psychotherapist will most likely be treated according to principles derived from Freudian psychoanalysis. Many psychologists and psychiatrists who work according to these "psychoanalytically oriented" principles may have forgotten that Freud devised psychoanalysis more as a research method than a therapy. According to Freud's investigative technique, the analyst first *listens* to the patient. As he reveals himself, the patient gives the analyst a picture first of the problems of which he is aware, then generally reveals conflicts and feelings of which he is *not* consciously aware. The analyst's main job is to figure out how unconscious feelings and conflicts are causing the patient's life problems and to help the patient become aware of them.

All psychotherapists know that merely *becoming aware* of your hitherto unconscious feelings (like hating your mother or fearing "castration" by your father) does not automatically make your problems vanish. Many other theoretical concepts have been developed by psychoanalysts to explain how unconscious feelings, once discovered by the patient, actually cease to dominate his life. If you study the cases of patients who get better in psychoanalysis or psychoanalytically oriented therapy you find that they do not merely become consciously aware of unconscious feelings they have hitherto avoided knowing about. They also:

1. Begin to feel about the analyst as they have earlier felt about a vital person in their lives, a parent. (This is called developing a "transference relationship" with the analyst.) Feelings about one important person in their lives are transferred to another, brought to consciousness and analyzed.
2. Successful patients also come to share the analyst's attitude that despite some discomfort they can and will become aware of the upsetting unconscious feelings and express them, because this would be a step toward getting better. (This is referred to as forming a "therapeutic alliance.")
3. Successful patients also prove able to find new ways to live which are more gratifying to them than the old; these new patterns of behavior are *not* so dominated by unconscious conflicts and needs as the old ways have been.

I was trained according to these conceptions, and I believe in them still. I have found my psychoanalytic training invaluable in teaching me to *listen* to the patient, to figure out what is bothering him, and *not* to impose my own values upon him. But I have always been disturbed at the reluctance of most psychoanalytically trained psychotherapists to go beyond these basic principles in working with young people. After all, once we have used our investigative techniques and have gotten an understanding of the patient's problems (conscious *and* unconscious), must we remain researchers, or are we justified in becoming more active in our dealings with him? The researcher role is *safer*. I agree with my colleagues that we must not "moralize," tell anyone *how* to live. Adolescents feel this way even more strongly than psychoanalysts. But nothing makes a confused adolescent turn away from psychotherapy more surely than a therapist who remains silent, ungiving, a nobody. The most common complaint I have heard from adolescents who have tried psychotherapy is that they found the therapists remote, cold, *impersonal*. "Every session was the same—I went and sat and tried to think of what to say, and the psychiatrist mostly just nodded and said nothing. After awhile I figured this was just wasting my parents' money. I could get more out of telling my hangups to a friend. So I quit!"

Picture the situation. An adolescent taking LSD and mescaline, close to dropping out of school. He has little time with his parents; for years there has been little close communication going on between them. This is true even in many families without unusually severe problems. Afraid of his parents' anger when they find out about the tripping and wanting to avoid hurting them, he keeps silent. Afraid of being expelled from school, he does not confide in his guidance counselor either. Perhaps he is fortunate: his falling grades and loss of motivation to do schoolwork result in a suggestion by the high school guidance counselor to the parent that they consult a professional, a psychologist or psychiatrist, to see what can be done. Or maybe the parents decide to seek help for him on their own.

Now the boy visits the psychiatrist. He is hoping he will find someone he can trust, someone who seems human, who can understand him. How cruel to find someone distant, bland, and unrevealing of himself. And even if the therapist is quite friendly and warm, he has been trained to keep more or less silent, to listen, to let the patient do the talking. He does not moralize or dictate, he does not play the authority. But his training has specifically and concretely taught him *not* to reveal much of himself. Too often this technique alienates the patient, and therapy grinds on fruitlessly or, if the patient is bolder, he quits. And now the adolescent, short on patience and perseverance anyway because he is an adolescent, feels he has tried the "therapy trip" and that it failed. So now he is less willing to try it again.

Adolescents are not adults. They are still trying to find out how to become adults. There is a tremendous amount they don't know about how adults live and feel. Too many of them are not getting enough direct input of honest data about adult life values and feelings from their parents. An average of *five minutes a day* of direct communication between adolescents and their parents has been the result of a survey I conducted. And five minutes a day is *not* enough, even if your father were a zen master and could fill the five minutes with incredibly compact messages covering the meaning of life. On top of this, adolescents are getting conflicting information about life values from the mass media and other kids.

In short, adolescents don't know enough about how *real* adults feel about their *real* lives. And when they get into psychotherapy they meet still another adult who seems benign but who tells them nothing about how it feels to live his own life. We know, of course, that communication goes on between people anyway, even without direct verbal messages. Communications research gives ample evidence that we are telling each other about ourselves all the time through *everything* we say and do. So the young person in psychotherapy too often is left to *infer* what sort of person his therapist is from the small cues he is offered. He gropes for something solid to relate to, but gets nothing he can grasp.

"Why doesn't he [my father, my therapist] tell me directly what he really feels? Doesn't he care enough about me to let me know him? Why is he hiding himself?"

In any relationship between adolescent and adult the adolescent will expect the adult to act like an adult. He may *want* and *need* the adult to lead and guide him, even though he may start off all set to rebel against any manifestation of leadership by the adult. Most adolescents will accept guidance from adults who are not afraid to relate to adolescents as *people* to *people*, but they often run into other adult styles of dealing with adolescents, the adult as dictator or as moralizer, or the adult as *nothing*. A fifteen-year-old boy who quit school describes this latter role:

"My guidance counselor in high school really bugged me. I had one meeting with her for less than half an hour, and she just approved my program. She didn't say anything to me at all about how I was doing in my courses. Then she called in my parents and told *them* I wasn't living up to my potential, and my I.Q. If she had a criticism of me, why didn't she call *me* in and tell me?

"After I ran away from home, it was weird. My parents never even mentioned that I had run away. Once in a while it came out by accident, like 'You haven't had a shower since you came back!,' but never directly. I guess they expected me to quit school, because since I got back they just stopped waking me up for school. That was okay with me, I didn't like school anyway. But they never brought that up either."

What adolescents too rarely encounter is the adult who relates as a more experienced friend, able to relate to an adolescent as advisor and guide but without trying to *force* obedience to his own values. In this case the adult says:

"I am the product of my own life experiences and my own decisions, including mistakes. I care enough about you to share these with you and to guide and advise you. But I will not *force* you to be like me or to accept my values."

Parents who feel this way have much less difficulty with their adolescent children. So I don't meet many of these parents in my psychiatric practice because their adolescent children don't seem to need therapy nearly as often.

But how disturbing it is to me to hear Vic and Chester and Chris talk about their first attempts to get help from a psychiatrist and how they discovered that these therapists could not be real people with them any more than their parents could. But when confronted with a therapist who will be *himself* with them, these same adolescents will stay in therapy long enough to benefit. A therapeutic relationship must be a *real* relationship—and a real relationship requires real people.

In human relationships, how do you know the other person cares about you? Not only because he listens to you telling about yourself, but because he too reveals himself. He is not anonymous, *not* faceless. Especially with adolescents who are desperate for identification and guidance, we must be ourselves and make *real* relationships. This can be done without moralizing and dictating. And it can sometimes be done even after young people have been disappointed by a previous failure to find anything real or sustaining in the relationship with a previous therapist. When they come to our School, many of the very same young people do make relationships with their teachers and with me and learn how to reveal themselves. In our place the reaching out is *mutual*. The adolescent is not expected to expose his feelings without the same contribution from us.

I have been warned that if I use psychoanalytic jargon in these pages, I should be prepared to define whatever terms I employ. I have no great confidence in my ability to define what "identification" might be. But I can describe what I have observed. Many adolescents who come to me for therapy show a tremendous hunger to find out how adults feel about the way they live. They ask specific questions about every aspect of my life as a psychiatrist. And they don't stop there. They want to know all about me as a man, too, and as a husband, lover, and father.

It is therapeutic to explore with patients the reasons for their questions. It is human to answer them. I do both, and I encourage teachers and parents to do both. The young patient actually *needs* the information he is asking for in order to learn how an adult functions. Too often the young patient becomes mortally fed up with getting no replies, only more questions, and if he is not hopelessly passive he quits therapy. Many of my Freudian colleagues report (off the record) that they realize you can't impose a rigid nonresponse technique upon adolescents or they will quit therapy. So they have learned to be more open with young patients, modifying the technique they learned in training. But they do it on their own, against the trend of their training, and wonder if they are doing the right thing.

In individual work with young people I do not hide my own feelings and beliefs. Where they might be useful, I refer to them and we discuss them. I also find out, of course, why the patient wants to know and why he has doubts about the kind of adult he will become. I am a therapist *and* person to him. This frees therapy from the rigid bonds of a restricting classical technique. There is no more concern with "what can be revealed"—none at all. I have found that when the therapist puts himself into the therapy, the patient generally does so as well, and therapy moves much more quickly. The "feeling-out" phase ("Can I trust this doctor?") is much more quickly past, and we can get down to interpersonal business.

For the therapist unused to this more open technique, the old guardedness must be overcome. This takes practice and preferably some supervision from someone who is used to being himself with patients. The most practical way to get to this might be for a traditional therapist to join a well-run encounter group (unlike the one I attended and described in Chapter 8) and *experience* first-hand the therapeutic effects of openness on the part of a skilled and trained group therapist. Therapists I know who have tried this feel it has helped them become more human with their patients. Once comfortable in being yourself with patients the experience of a richer and freer therapeutic alliance validates itself.

To me, an ideal therapist for adolescents is someone who is a successful human being. He has found a way to live that gratifies him, makes him exude life-is-good vibrations. He feels good and he looks alive. He is someone an adolescent looks at and feels "this guy has got something." This ideal therapist, in Erikson's terms, has himself mastered the problems posed by his own human need to develop in a complex society. Somehow he has developed a firm sense of *identity* (who and what he is), he can be *intimate* without conflict (he can love), he has generated something (his own children or a way of giving to the young), he has found ego *integrity*. In other terms, the ideal therapist must be someone who is *authentic*, who is fully functioning. This is hard to find. But I repeat R. D. Laing's definition of psychotherapy (*The Politics of Experience*); this definition is my guide:

"*Psychotherapy must remain the obstinate attempt of two people to recover the wholeness of being human by the relationship between them.*"

If the therapist is not whole, he can't help the patient get further than he himself has gone. When you are not whole, sooner or later every intimate human relationship will get close to your wounds, it will begin to reawaken your inner awareness of weakness and incompleteness. You will guard yourself, block further penetration, and the patient will sense the wall inside you. He will feel rejected or he will avoid going further into this place in you because he does not want to hurt you or to risk losing what he already has with you. And the "wholeness of being human," he finds out, cannot be recovered between the two of you.

The word is "wholeness." And wholeness is not the same as fragmentation. Analysis is fragmentation. When it works, it is because some psychoanalysts are *whole* people and manage to let themselves show *wholeness* to their patients even though using a method designed for analysis, breaking down and fragmenting what is experienced. Recent critics of psychoanalysis like Eysenck have shown that whatever school of thought a psychoanalyst comes from, it does not seem to make much difference in the results of his work. About half the patients get better whether they are treated by Jungian,

Adlerian, Freudian, existential, or any other method. To me this is good reason to suspect that the secret of cure is largely found in the kind of *person* the analyst or therapist is, *not* in the school he attended. In a fascinating study performed a few years ago in a psychiatric clinic, it was found that the patients of certain therapists tended to get no better, even get worse, despite the fact that these therapists had identical training with other therapists whose patients got better. The researchers, devilishly clever, then gave some basic therapy training to some people who were warm and giving, genuine human beings; these people proved almost as successful as fully trained therapists with similar personal qualities.

Not all patients are going to be able to become whole. But if they are even to have the chance, the therapist must be whole and fully human. Because whatever the symptoms that bring a patient to see you, you are not only showing him how to give them up, you are teaching him *wholeness*. I am belaboring this point because the new watchword among our youth is wholeness. Kids are rising up everywhere and rejecting fragmentation, contradiction, and tolerance of evil. When Boston University students in the school newspaper attack a newly appointed trustee of the university for being a board member of several corporations which have been holding tin miners or oil workers or banana-pickers in abject poverty, they are refusing to fragment the situation by thinking in the way the board thought when they appointed him:

"He *did* indirectly participate in this imperialism, but he is influential after all, and he will help raise money for the university." The students want the board to be *all* democratic or have no board at all. When the Tufts students demonstrate to get more black men employed in a construction project on campus, they are demanding that we *practice* what we preach, that democracy be *whole*, that we do *not* split principle and practice. When these young people come to an adult for guidance, they want him *whole*. If they think he is not, they generally quit.

Fortunately, in some training programs we are nowadays seeing more emphasis on the idea that it is as much the therapist's *personality* which helps the patient as his training and experience. There should be much more emphasis in the training of psychotherapists upon the creative use of *self* in therapy.

Of course, challenging situations arise when working directly and openly. At times something a patient does makes me angry with him. When I am angry, even though I am a psychotherapist, I feel the anger in my body like anyone else does, and my anger is revealed in my tone of voice, my gestures, and my posture. There is no concealment of feeling possible in psychotherapy any more than in any other human relationship. An assumed neutrality would not conceal my anger from my patient—so the anger must be revealed and used to help the patient.

#### BRAD, AN ADOLESCENT PATIENT

He is the sixteen-year-old schizophrenic boy referred to earlier, who had been hospitalized over a year after a long period of using LSD, speed, and heroin. He came for therapy for three months and improved, then dropped out of therapy for two months. He has called me at this moment to ask for more help.

*Brad*: "I feel terrible, I am getting paranoid again. I feel people are after me, waiting to get me. They come in cars and park outside my yard and wait for me to come out. They are hoods, they beat up hippies. They want to hurt me, maybe kill me. My friend gave me a gun. One night I got so angry at some cat crying that I actually shot the cat. I think I killed it—put it out of its misery."

*Myself*: "I can see you feel very angry and scared. You have

missed some appointments with me. Are you taking the thorazine I prescribed for you?"
**Brad**: "No, I threw it away. And I didn't feel like coming here any more. I can't stand these groups and all these people."

Brad had been seeing me individually as well as attending an art class and a weekly group therapy session. At the last group meeting he attended, he revealed how he went down to a ghetto neighborhood over and over again in his hippy clothes, almost begging to be attacked. The group told Brad he was trying to provoke a situation where he'd be attacked and then feel justified in hurting or killing somebody. I had pointed out to Brad that he was trying to recreate the situation of his childhood in which his alcoholic father beat him— (he later began to have dreams of killing his father). He agreed this was so, then stopped coming for therapy.

**Myself**: "Yes, in the last group session they gave you a bad time over provoking the hoods in Roxbury to attack you. That got you angry, I believe."
**Brad**: "Yes, nobody can stop me from what I want to do. I'm not coming back to the group. I threw away your thorazine— it makes me too calm; I don't feel like I want to feel when I take it."

Now I am feeling some anger at Brad for throwing away the controls I have given him—our sessions and the thorazine, which previously controlled his rage and murderous fantasies. I also know he can feel my anger; he is sensitive to my feelings.
**Myself**: "Brad, you make me angry. You are telling me that you won't let me help you control your rage at your father. You are saying, 'Shep, I won't let you take away my dream of killing my father and then suffering the penalty for it.' I feel angry when you ask me for help and then don't let me help you."
**Brad**: "You're right. That dream of killing is always in the back of my mind. It is very hard to give it up. He deserves it! And those hoods deserve it, to know that they can't get away

with attacking people. When I pull out the gun they'll know they went too far. I'll have the power then, not them! . . ."
*Myself*: "Brad, without therapy and the medication I gave you, you are dangerous to others and yourself. I want you to see me regularly again, take the medication, and give up the Russian roulette. I don't want you or anyone else to be hurt. If you can't get back under control on your own, I'll get you back into the hospital."

Brad then agreed to therapy and medication. I made sure his mother knew about the situation, including the gun.

With a very confused and disturbed young patient it is even more important that feelings felt by the therapist should be dealt with openly. Sensing my anger, Brad could easily have become convinced that I too am against him; he could feed his paranoid fantasy that everyone is out to hurt him. As I revealed my anger at being rendered helpless as his therapist, I also revealed my continued concern for his welfare. I feel that his agreement to continue therapy on my terms means he is going once again to try to control his murderous rage. He must come to terms with it, or he cannot live in society.

The same applies to all feeling the therapist has about a patient, including sexual feelings. Ruth is a nineteen-year-old girl who came into therapy because she felt depressed and unsatisfied with her life. She had recently lost her boyfriend, who left her for an older woman. Ruth was very attractive and sexually provocative. She talked a great deal about how much she enjoyed doing "all that fucking." It was clear after only two sessions that she needed to feel a sexual response from all men, including me. When the third session began, she entered wearing a more revealing dress than before, and sat down quietly. She was silent, which is uncharacteristic of Ruth. I started feeling a strong sexual response to the way Ruth looked that day. The subject of her sexual feelings toward me had not yet been brought up.

*Myself*: "Something is going on in this silence. Do you feel it?"
*Ruth*: "Yes. I don't feel like talking about my boyfriend or my parents or any of that stuff."
*Myself*: "What do you feel like talking about?" (Ruth is silent.)
*Myself*: "I'm feeling something in the air between us today. I feel sexually turned on by you. Have you been feeling something like that?"
*Ruth*: "Well, yes. I get thoughts about a sex scene between us. I mean, whether it would be possible and if I turn you on, and how you would be to fuck. It seems important to me that you are attracted to me. . . . I know your wife is a great woman. I met her once. She's so attractive, and a dancer and all that. She's really a *woman*. I feel like a little girl, that I don't know anything and I can't really do anything. . . . I am attracted to older men with wives sometimes. I like to know I turn them on, that I can have them if I want to. I get into these situations between an older man and another woman. Maybe that's why I'm so depressed about losing my boyfriend—because he picked an older woman over me, someone who knows more about life."
*Myself*: "I think getting involved with married men, taking them away from a wife or an older woman, is part of your problem. If you lose him, you feel depressed. If you get him, you feel guilty over what you did to his woman. So even though I find you sexually attractive, I am going to stay your therapist and not your lover. You have a right to have a man all your own, who will really give himself to you completely, not someone who already loves someone else."

After this, Ruth settled down to discussing her rivalry with her mother over her father's attention, which was a major source of her difficulty. I feel that if the sexual seduction game had remained unacknowledged between us, she would not have been able to move into seeing the underlying reasons for her seductiveness, at least not for a long time. I am absolutely sure that if I had not admitted my *own* feelings of arousal, she would not have admitted hers.

I make a general policy of revealing my own feelings to patients whenever I feel those feelings enter into the therapeutic relationship. I also discuss my own past experiences, including mistakes. Working with adolescents I am aware that I am inevitably cast in three roles, whether I ask for it or not:

1. Therapist—revealer of unconscious conflicts and feelings.
2. Parent figure—someone who is older and more experienced and who has faced the kinds of crises and decisions the patient is facing. How did he solve them?
3. Person—someone who has the same kinds of desires and feelings the patient has and is not afraid to acknowledge them.

And I am all of these. I need hide none of the feelings connected with any of these aspects of myself.

# 10 › The Divine Self: Yoga and Meditation at the School

MANY OF OUR KIDS at the School are interested in mystical and Eastern approaches to the spiritual side of life. There is a deep feeling among the young that our American society deals with everything by analyzing, fragmenting, dividing and subdividing. The kids complain that mother and dad set up life in boxes: work, school, home, city, suburb, vacation in the country. Nature is for vacations; God is thought about when in Church, usually on Sunday only, if ever. Dad's job is technical, assisting in some tiny way to make something whose final use is not related to the family. Maybe he assists in the creation of missiles and warheads though he votes for the antiwar candidate every four years. The kids are feeling, "Why do we live this way? What are we doing?" And lots of parents feel this way too. In this atmosphere of affluence and disconnection, Eastern religions have an appeal. Kids have come to agree with Baba Ram Dass, who used to be Richard Alpert, that if you "change your head you change your life!" Wanting to change life, they change their heads. The idea is that if you change your attitude toward life, you can become free of some of the hassles arising from the money-work-anthill. By hanging looser, abandoning the quest for the big ice-cream cone in the sky, you can enjoy much more the here and now. Mothers and fathers are so involved in planning for the future, the time when the kids will all be out of college, or the mortgage will be paid, that at home there is not enough here and now. To these kids, that is what is the matter.

In line with my conviction that I can be some kind of a guide to the kids if I offer honestly my own beliefs and solutions, I began to teach yoga and meditation. I have been a believer in yoga and meditation for fifteen years, and I know what they have done for me. This was not a maneuver arising from a notion of "balanced curriculum" ("Let's get a little spiritual stuff in here, the kids would go for it . . .") but another attempt to let what is important in my life be shown to the kids. To me, being able to relax deeply, disengaging myself for awhile from overinvolvement with the details of my life, has been lifesaving. I have been teaching them those skills —how to take a vacation from your "ego-trip" and come back relaxed and refreshed. You become less a prisoner of your life style and its accumulated habits; having been away from it, you see it more objectively on your return from meditation. You might decide to change it or redecorate it.

Another important benefit from meditation is that meditation encourages peak experiences, which are enormously enriching. Maslow's work on peak experiences, as described in *Toward a Psychology of Being* indicates that there is a high correlation between creativity and peak experiences. In my experience there are several intercorrelated factors: creativity—peak experiences—mastery over one's ego trip.

Unlike the swamis from India I have known, I don't insist on my yoga students reading the Indian scriptures or learning the Sanskrit names for the yoga postures. I don't push them aggressively into harder and harder exercises either, like a football coach. That would be putting in a note of competitiveness and product orientation that is opposed to the very spirit of yoga. Rather, I let the students progress at their own rate, encouraging them to explore and deepen the mental states brought on by yoga postures and meditation. At the end of my weekly classes, I have added some trance-deepening techniques I learned from psychiatric hypnotherapy, which tends to help the kids let go for awhile of their tensions and painful self-awareness. Many kids have reported that they get higher at the end of yoga and meditation class than they do on grass, "and it's great to do it yourself, without needing drugs." Yoga and meditation do in fact change your state of consciousness, bring relief from the tendency to get bogged down in your troubles and your daily life. I find that return to my daily life is enjoyable after yoga, and I can live my life more deeply. I wanted the kids to see that, and a good many of them do. When the School finds its own quarters, we'll probably have daily yoga and meditation periods.

# PART 3 ›
# Somebody Knows What Is Best for You

# 11 › Adolescent Psychiatry as Transcultural Psychiatry

ADOLESCENTS TODAY have not been brought up under the same conditions as their parents. Adolescents have been exposed to television, more changes of address, more father and mother substitutes. They have had less "old-country awareness," less of grandmas and churches and synagogues. More babysitters, team teaching, audiovisual aids and cartoon shows. Less radio, less reading, less communication with their fathers and mothers.

Do you doubt that it is so different? A couple of months ago I asked a group of about a hundred teen-agers and their parents a few embarrassing questions: "How much time do you spend each day in direct verbal communication with your parents?" A hand rose in the rear of the room. "What do you mean by communication?" "Either you talking and your parents listening, or them talking and you listening." The consensus was about *five minutes* a day.

"How much time do you spend watching TV each day?" Two hours plus. Together we drew up a chart of daily involvements:

| | |
|---|---|
| 5 minutes | Parents |
| 2 hours | Teachers and other school staff |
| 2–3 hours | Friends |
| All the rest | Media: TV and stereo records and magazine and paperback books. |

A chart of my own teen-age communication patterns in Brooklyn, New York, 1943, would have shown less time with peers, much less with media, and more with parents and teachers. But my point here is not only that a lot of teen-agers live a quite different life style from the one their parents lived as teen-agers, but a more basic issue is involved. A creature and his environment form a natural system in which the creature develops. The environment forms him and he forms his environment—no other creature can dwell at the center of *his* unique system, hence no other creature can be fully aware of his system. Someone of the same age, raised in a similar family and neighborhood (a similar system) will understand his system best—but not completely. Genetic endowment, special early life experiences, illnesses, and traumata are different for everyone.

Parents and too often psychotherapists tend to operate by dominating the life systems of young people. This can be as dangerous as introducing rabbits to Australia or penicillin to the staphylococcus. Note that I have not said it is dangerous to offer advice, useful information, or a personal example to the young. What is dangerous is to assume the driver's seat, to overstress some segment of his life system and take control away from him. Give a youth a diagnosis, call him a schizophrenic, and now you will send him to a place where schizophrenics are kept, where others will relate to him not as a person in his own life system, but as a psychotic in a hospital system. Soon he will come to see himself this way as well. Will this help him? Think back to the highly regulated life system of the New Guinea tribe I talked about in the first chapter. When I heard that story of the intricate relationship of pigs and spirits and population, I was moved. I felt a longing inside myself, the kind of feeling a middle-aged American psychiatrist is vulnerable to. Wouldn't it be comfortable to be a member of such a tribe, where everything is regulated, where you always know what to do? "What has happened to the tribe since you lived with them?" I asked the anthropologist.

And he told me how the Australian government sent medical personnel and inoculated the babies so the infant mortality rate fell and there were more children to feed, and not enough food to feed them with. And they are all wearing Bermuda shorts these days too, imported from Australia with the shots.

These people had no chance to decide whether they *wanted* Bermuda shorts and inoculation of the infants. The district administrators decided these things for them. And apparently there was insufficient attention paid to how the children, now no longer dying in the same numbers early in infancy, would be fed. In America medical care for our Indians has also improved since the tribes roamed the plains. Though more Indian babies die than "Anglo" babies, the general standard of physical health of American Indians is no doubt higher than it was a hundred years ago. But the Indians have paid a high price for it. And so have the New Guinea tribesmen. And neither asked for the deal.

Here and there groups of simple people are wise enough to resist changes in their life systems. The residents of the volcanic island Tristan de Cunha were saved from almost certain death in an eruption a few years ago and removed to England. After a short time many of them went back to their island despite the likelihood of another eruption at any time which might destroy them all. And a religious sect of American Indians who use peyote as a sacramental drug refused to allow their peyote ceremony to be filmed by a sympathetic anthropologist, even though the film was to be used in Washington to help protect the ceremony from being outlawed. Despite promises of future benefit, the elders felt that the integrity of the group peyote experience should not be violated.

Man without his life system, without his context, is worthless. And violating the integrity of the life system of another person is a great crime. This is seen clearly by hippies and some anthropologists but not as yet by many of those who deal with young people. In America we have preached and lived independence and social mobility for a long time. Our society is fragmented. We can no longer regard our young people as members of the same life system that we ourselves belong to. We must treat their systems with the same respect as we want accorded to our own.

Young people become more and more aware as they grow up of the life systems of their elders—family, school, neighborhood, police, court, hospital. Many of them in adolescence reject these systems or more specifically they say, "I don't want to live within these systems the way older people do." The commonest error made by parents, school, officials, judges, and many psychiatrists is to attempt to force them to live with society's systems in the way *we* do. When anyone attempts to design his own life style, his own way of living in an environment, he is declaring his uniqueness as a person, and we will alienate him if we force him to change. Then we have a power struggle such as this one, between the long-haired teen-age boy and the school principal:

**SP:** "Hair must be worn a moderate length in this school."
**TAB:** "To *me* this is moderate."
**SP:** "Not to *me*. Get it cut so it doesn't hang over your ears."
**TAB:** "With this leather headband it doesn't touch my ears."
**SP:** "Cut it to one inch or less within one week or you're suspended."
One week passes.
**TAB:** "How's this?"
**SP:** "Now you have no hair. You shaved it off—*that's* not moderate! You're suspended till it grows to one inch long!"

SP has now demonstrated two things he wanted TAB to know:

1. *He* controls behavior in the school.
2. He can kick you out of his system if you don't conform.

SP has also demonstrated a few things he did not want to demonstrate:

1. School is *his* system, not TAB's.
2. He cares more about what's *on* the head than what's *in* it.
3. He does not respect the integrity of TAB's life system, hence he must be regarded as the enemy.
4. If you want to be free to relate to your own system, better not go back to school—at least not *his* school.

TAB has demonstrated a few things:

1. He won't let another person's rules control the length of his hair.
2. His own life style is more important to him than school.
3. He knows that attempting to force another person to change his life style is wrong.

Over the past fifteen years I have worked with adolescents as a psychiatrist. I have come to know them in court clinics, training schools, hospitals, and in private practice. Most of the young people I have known are refugees from various authorities who want to change their systems of life without understanding either the history or values of those systems.

Often parents cannot accept a style of life in their child which they themselves programmed him into. When he reaches adolescence they reject the child for being the person they unwittingly trained him to be. A good example is Harry's story:

Harry is very tall, very gaunt, and at the time I knew him, a ragged fiery-eyed vagabond. His intelligence is outstanding. Harry is now living the marijuana-LSD life in the slums of a large city. A warrant is out for his arrest for violating probation as a school offender (not attending) but so far he has avoided arrest. Harry's father was jealous from the first of the love and attention Harry got from his mother. He would discipline Harry severely and unexpectedly—that is, when he was around. But most of the time the "don'ts" were left to Harry's mother, who felt closer to Harry than to her husband and overprotected the boy. As soon as father would issue a prohibition she would help Harry get around it on the sly. This policy achieved several things, Harry told me:

1. It made him go to mother, not father, for whatever he wanted.
2. It made him nevertheless feel contempt for mother, who always gave in even when his demands were unreasonable.
3. It gave him a taste for using people and making them give in.
4. It also made him feel hatred and fear of his father.

When Harry reached his teens, the rules began to be made by others—the school department, then the police, then the probation officer. By now Harry wanted to demonstrate that he could still get around all the rules and enjoy the loved-one status no matter what the authorities said. He is no longer in school, he is guilty of several felonies (drug dealing and use), and when he is found he will probably serve time in a "training school."

What is the point? By the time Harry reached sixteen he had learned to live in his own particular style within the permissive system in which his mother brought him up, defying authority as he had successfully defied his father. Forceful attempts to change his life style are now too late. They will make him rebel secretly or openly.

Psychiatry has understood in depth that the earliest interactions of parent and child have a great deal to do with the shaping of the life style the child will later adopt. Once formed, arbitrary or authoritarian attempts to change this life style will be ineffective, will in fact polarize the behavior, making it still more extreme. This is seen when police are used arbitrarily in university demonstrations. Of course many adolescents have developed life styles that will get them into serious trouble with society. Delinquency, drug use, careless sexual promiscuity, dropping out of school are all patterns which can result in damage to one's life in the larger society. As a psychiatrist I have tried to find out how to help young people change these patterns. It has become obvious to me that lawmaking, threats, and force are not effective in making teen-agers feel the need to change these life styles.

What took me longer to realize was that standard-brand psychotherapy is generally not helpful to adolescents either. Few hippies, delinquents, or drug users are helped very much by hours spent every week with psychiatrists, even if they can afford private help or tolerate waiting for months to be seen at the local mental health clinic. And what disturbed me most was to realize that the Freudian techniques I learned in my psychiatric and psychoanalytic training seemed almost useless with the much larger group of confused adolescent seekers who found their way to my office looking for someone who could help them evolve some kind of a life that would express their talents and qualities—a life that would give pleasure and have some meaning. When these young seekers are highly creative people, the search for a meaningful life is even more poignant. Even in the arts, it is so hard to find training that does not stifle the free expression of talent under formal controls, much less find a way to get society to take notice of what you want to say. And it is just as hard to find a therapist who will respect your life style as it is to find that kind of education.

The techniques I learned in my psychiatric training were derived directly from Freud's psychoanalytic techniques, or at least what were said to be Freud's techniques. I was taught the usual kind of amiable watchful impassiveness, which give the patient as few clues as possible as to my own feelings. I can remember how eagerly I espoused these techniques at first. I knew that most of the time with my first patients I knew so little about what was going on that a technique requiring me mostly to nod and be silent was at least safe, if not demonstrably helpful. My psychoanalytic training in particular was for me a five-year exercise in submission and passivity. The atmosphere of reverence for the master was overpowering. Very few of the psychoanalytic candidates-in-training felt we knew enough to challenge anything. Picture an art school dominated by reverence for Rembrandt, where all later work is regarded as of minor significance. Here you must make Rembrandt copies or fail to graduate. It seems obvious that art mirrors life—when life changes, art changes. The same man does not make T'ang pottery horses and ten-foot Campbell soup cans. But when I was in training, it was as if man and life styles had not changed from Vienna 1910 to Boston 1960. At the point where Erik Erikson's ideas on identity formation were being discussed Talmudically ("Freud really said it all first!") I felt as if a giant hand were lifting me from my seat and propelling me from the psychoanalytic seminar. I turned in my resignation. My closest friends asked me if my analyst approved my leaving ("acting out," it was called, of course). The institute never inquired of me why I quit.

As I look back on my decision to leave psychoanalytic training, I see it as a first step in my search for a new way of working with young people. I wanted to find out how I could help them see better ways of becoming what *they* wanted to become. I did not want to be part of an authority system which accepts only a narrow range of life styles, which is how Freudian psychoanalysis impresses me. It was already clear to me as I left the institute that the psychoanalytic system was an unbearable intrusion into my own life style. And the younger you are, the harder it is to feel you may be right and the authority may be wrong. Too many young talented people have surrendered their creative energy and impulse-lives under this kind of pressure. If you seek therapy you must find a therapist who understands your life style and respects it. He must see what is unique in your way of living, he must believe in your ability to make *your* system work. What I heard said in the psychoanalytic institute was, "This is the way to work. Learn it." I did not see understanding of the unique talents and gifts of each candidate. My rebellion was against the crushing of my own life style in the name of psychoanalytic technique. To me, psychotherapy is an art. I had to do it my own way.

My first job after completing two years of residency in adult psychiatry and two years of child psychiatry was in a court clinic. Massachusetts has a most progressive system with some seventeen clinics in district courts, one in a juvenile court, one in a superior court. In these clinics people can be seen by a psychiatrist who will tell the court if they need psychiatric help, and many offenders can get psychotherapy in the court clinic free of charge. The clinic I began work in was in an industrial slum area of Cambridge; it was the second court clinic in existence. I was for a while the only psychiatrist in the clinic.

The bulk of my court patients in Cambridge were teen-agers from poor Italian and Irish families with many children. They were in for stealing or hooking school or running away. When I got into the interview room with them, they turned out to be completely unused to talking to anyone about feelings. All the verbal finesse I had accumulated in my training with middle-class educated patients was useless here. These kids had never known anyone like me in all their lives. But what was worse, I had very little awareness of what *their* lives were like, yet I was supposed to make recommendations to the judge—recommendations which would change their future for them. Should they be committed to our inadequate training schools? Be sentenced to probation? Did they need foster homes? Or would they stay out of trouble if the psychiatrist (myself) could get through to them?

The Cambridge court clinic was my first experience with the culture of poverty. My next assignment bathed me in it. I founded the Roxbury court clinic in Boston's black ghetto, working out of an ancient and decrepit courthouse. Once again I was for a while a one-man clinic. And here the stories of desertion, grinding poverty, violence, and despair were much more serious. Oscar Lewis has since written about these life styles in several books (*La Vida, Children of Sanchez, Five Families*), and the civil-rights struggle in America has made us aware of what his concept, "the culture of poverty," really means. The people of Roxbury are largely black. As in Harlem or Watts, the atmosphere is full of smoldering resentment and violence. The white people referred to our court clinic suffered from the same kind of degradation as the black, with the exception of racial prejudice.

It was in Roxbury that I finally learned that I was doing what is now called "transcultural psychiatry." I learned that we in our clinic could help these oppressed and suffering people only if we could understand their styles of life and translate them to the judge and the probation officers. We had to show the court why jobless black fathers deserted their pregnant girls, why black teen-agers felt no guilt stealing from white-owned stores. We had to show the court it was enforcing white middle-class law upon these people. We were able to help a good many people this way, but all of us working in the clinic knew that a social revolution would be needed to make a real change for them.

Roxbury taught me that understanding a culture in depth is absolutely essential if you want to be of any help at all to anyone from that culture. You also have to know a culture well before you can see when you *can't* help someone from that culture.

Working in Roxbury made me feel like learning about other styles of life, other races. I went to Hawaii as chief of a mental health team working in the state prison and youth training schools near Honolulu. There I got acquainted with people of many races and combinations—Hawaiians, Samoans, Filipinos, Chinese, Japanese, Koreans, Okinawans, third-generation descendants of transplanted New England missionaries and end-of-the-road Southern California wanderers. For years my wife and I had been yoga students. When we got to Hawaii we couldn't find a yoga class we wanted to take, so we became yoga teachers. I got interested in hypnosis and relaxation training, and I began to mix some of these techniques with my teaching of yoga and meditation. The word went around the hippie subculture of Honolulu, and soon our yoga classes became filled with young people, seekers—interested in the mystical, the experiential, "turning on," and grooving with nature. Some of these kids became my patients and friends. From them I learned something I am trying to express in this book —that youth itself has become a subculture in our country. *Working with young people is transcultural psychiatry* even when those young people come from middle-class suburbs. In fact, when I, a forty-four-year-old man of Brooklyn Jewish middle-class origins, treat an eighteen-year-old boy of Brooklyn Jewish middle-class origins, it is still transcultural psychiatry. Even though this boy comes from my home town and belongs to the same religion and social class I came from, his values are bound to be very different from my own. In an article in *The New York Times Magazine,* Paul Goodman told a fascinating story. He gave a graduate seminar at the New School for Social Research in New York. The subject was "Professionalism." The students heard a doctor, a lawyer, an engineer, a journalist, an architect, and others explain the "obstacles that increasingly stood in the way of honest practice, and their own life experience in circumventing them." Goodman went on to report that the graduate students not only did not understand or sympathize with the struggles of these professionals, the class unanimously rejected them. The young students expressed the feeling that professions are "concepts of repressive society and 'linear thinking'—it was important only to be human, and all else would follow." The students had become "absurd," as Goodman put it, or "alienated."

The popular press has seized upon the fact that there are at least two kinds of "alienated" kids these days, perhaps quoting and oversimplifying the work of Kenneth Keniston of Yale. He tells us that some of the young radical demonstrators in the college riots are healthy radicals who are working for change in an integrated and planned way, while other young rebels are "sick." Angry, frustrated, unhappy products of empty family lives, these kids turn out to confront the cops, trying to find themselves through finding a cause. From my young friends in Roxbury and Hawaii I learned that young people belong to *many* subcultures—some are built around LSD and marijuana, some around mysticism and meditation, some around political action. A few are dedicated to violence and destruction. In every one of these little tribes I have known, there is a core of young leaders who fit Keniston's description in his book *The Young Radicals*. These leaders are not "sick" but have identified themselves deeply with certain goals they believe in. Groups have formed around them. Ken Kesey as portrayed by Tom Wolfe in *The Electric Kool-Aid Acid Test* fits this description.

Some members of these groups are obviously "sick." They rely on the subculture of alienation to furnish a life for them to live, a scene in which to exist. So grass, hash, acid, political action, transcendental meditation are for these particular kids *needed*—the "sick" have only *needs*, not *choices*. At least, that is one psychiatric definition of "sick."

Working with young people, I can identify some of both kinds, leaders and needers. But the point is that adolescents now belong to cultures different from my own; *none* can be understood in the same terms my parents understood (or misunderstood) me.

Why not? Not only because things have changed in American life since these kids' parents (and myself) were adolescents, but because things are changing more and more rapidly. And a curious change has occurred lately in the confrontations between adolescents and psychotherapists. I can remember when these encounters (particularly in the court clinic) sounded like this:

*Psychotherapist*: "You seem to have some problems."
*Adolescent*: "No, I don't."

*P*: "Well, you dropped out of school and now you got arrested for running away."
*A*: "I just got fed up with school and I don't think my parents' rules are fair either. So I took off!"
*P*: "Let's look a little deeper into your feelings about your parents and school. Maybe you have some feelings you are not conscious of that made you take off and get into trouble."
*A*: "That's ridiculous! I just got fed up and took off!"

And it took a lot of work to show such young people that there are in each of us whole realms of unconscious feelings and ideas which govern our actions. But lately there has been a shift in the attitude of many young people about unconscious mental life. Many of them now know that this realm exists: Some explore it with drugs, some with meditation. But they feel that most therapists, for all their talk of the unconscious, are unable to experience this world as they do. And they see this world as infinite, not limited to the Freudian dynamics of mother and father and baby and sister in the first five years of life.

Don is an example of this new outlook. Now in his early twenties, he has survived four therapists (I am one) since it became clear during his early teens that he would never become the professional man his socially prominent parents always wanted him to be. A most successful surgeon, his father looked forward to Don becoming a doctor—especially since his first son died in infancy. When Don developed as a dreamy, unassertive little boy, his father drove him hard toward school success and scientific interest, then finally gave up in disgust when Don did not excel in school. Don's mother, a cold woman whose main interests are her appearance and her social activities, was no more successful in getting close to him. Although she did not reject him as his father did, she considered him as weak, an inevitable failure.

By the time he reached sixteen, Don was doing very poorly

in school. He became deeply depressed. His view was that life is a tragic illusion: people are all selfish, cold, rejecting. "They build you up so they can screw you." He became a perennial victim, a self-proclaimed loser. Other psychiatrists gave him shock therapy. In my own two years of work with Don, I was able only to keep him out of the hospital and to act as some kind of buffer between him and the unrealistic demands of his parents.

Recently, Don started studying astrology—a subject that had long fascinated him. Feeling doomed, he wanted to know more about fate. Within three weeks after the first lesson, he looked more alert, seemed more open. I asked him about the change. His reply was: "You know, I can see now why I am alive, and also why my parents are on this earth!" When I pressed him further Don explained that studying his own astrological chart had showed him that his own mission for the sake of his parents was to help them to learn to *give*; this is what they must learn from their present incarnation as a part of the process of spiritual perfection, which takes many lifetimes. For himself, while helping them to give, he must learn to accept his solitariness and his moodiness and nonetheless become independent.

I was amazed. All my many hours of therapy with Don had not given him these awarenesses—and these were *accurate*. Don had accepted from the zodiac what he had not taken from Freud. What had happened was that the astrologer who taught Don had been from the very first deeply interested in Don and intuitively sympathetic with his struggle. When she met him she knew nothing about him, but she walked over, placed a hand on his shoulder and said; "Oh, you *do* have a problem with an authoritarian father! Tell me, when were you born?" From that moment, Don was hooked. From an unusually intense relationship with his teacher, a unique person, Don began to change. He has done steadily better since that moment.

Many young people I know nowadays are just as ready as

Don to believe in the existence of many realms of mind and soul: the mystical and spiritual are everyday topics of discussion for them. When I arranged a class in yoga and meditation for teen-agers last fall in a local church, over fifty kids averaging fifteen years old joined the class. Most of these kids had not used psychedelic drugs. But mysticism and the spiritual have lately become major concerns for many young people, including the sons and daughters of chemists and computer programmers. Marshall McLuhan says this "TV generation" of adolescents share a new electronic existence, they live in a "global village" in which a "mystical participation" in life has become a goal, not success in terms of careers and salaries, even though these are the terms still used by their parents and high school guidance counselors.

Almost all the young people I work with these days are interested in the mystical. Many of them have sought what Maslow calls peak experiences, some using mind-expanding drugs. Some have come to grief through the complications of this path. Others have gone deeply into transcendental meditation, yoga, and zen buddhism. The effect of these experiments and countless highs on grass has been that as a group they are *less* interested in goals like patriotism, achievement in work and school, social popularity, and reputation than their "normal" peers. They consider such goals to be small, even insignificant, and definitely misleading. They have become aware of values they see as cosmic—serenity, mindlessness, openness to experience, and creative expression. These young people must be dealt with respectfully as members of another culture from mine. They come to the School to learn what they wish, to partake of a therapy experience to the extent that they can and will. As with foreign visitors, I must not assume my own ways are superior or more knowing. And time after time they have moved to help each other in ways I was sure would fail, and they made me see that their perceptions of what would be helpful for one another were much more accurate than mine.

# 12 › The Question of Authority

OUR TEEN-AGERS live in a world controlled by others. Parents and school principals, judges and legislators make and enforce rules for behavior which young people are expected to follow. Marijuana is forbidden; using it is a crime despite the increasing evidence that it is not harmful. High school students must take English, mathematics, history, and French whether they see a use for these or not. Boys will be drafted though they don't want to kill or be killed. They will be suspended from school for wearing long hair and be unable to find jobs for the same reason, despite fair employment practices laws.

So far, most of the teen-agers I have talked to report that parents and educators not only refuse to let them help make rules governing their own behavior but will not even discuss how they arrive at the rules they make *for* them. Wherever they occur, the rebellions and demonstrations in schools and colleges represent the demand of young people to participate in making the rules for their own lives. Life as prescribed by the elders seems to more and more young people to be empty and meaningless. Studying subjects you are not interested in so you can get a job you don't want seems uninspiring until you contemplate how it would feel to be drafted to fight in a war you don't believe in. These are your alternatives unless you start taking over control of your own life. When *you* decide what you want to learn and what you will do with your knowledge it all means more to you. But will society let you decide how to conduct your life? It will not, especially if you are an adolescent. High schools (public, parochial, and private) are training schools in conformity. It is taken for granted in most high schools that all decisions relating to students will be made by administrators without consulting students. And when students revolt against this arbitrary government, no one is as surprised as the principal and his staff.

Last year I conducted a youth forum in a New England high school. This was a weekly group discussion open to anyone in the high school, students or faculty. The idea was that in the forum anyone could discuss anything of personal or group importance. The only rule was that all comments be honest and all reactions be equally honest. In short, a kind of group therapy in a high school. What developed in this group was fascinating. For the first several months, personal problems simply did not arise though most of the group members felt the purpose of our meetings should be to discuss and solve personal problems. What arose every session was the collective feeling of the students that they had no role at all in handling their own affairs in the school. Their student council was a rubber stamp, a country club, a popularity contest. Decisions affecting all would be made and announced and no student knew how they were arrived at or why they were made. The students in the forum felt frustrated and angry about this but they did not know how to change it. Occasionally petitions would be passed around or a few students would go to see the principal on one issue or another, but it seemed that no real change ever occurred.

The astonishing part of all this was that the school was very progressive and run by a dynamic young principal. When the students finally decided how to seek a greater voice in their own affairs, the principal was ready to cooperate. It was simply that there was no precedent, no habit of students working together with administrators, so administrators just went on making decisions by themselves. And young people just went on complying, all the time feeling, as Friedenberg would put it, "colonialized."

And of course the habit of the middle-aged deciding what is good for adolescents applies in almost all universities as well. Just the other day an intelligent girl told me about the college where she has been admitted. Apparently it became clear that a new freshman dormitory would not be completed by registration day, so girls living near the college would have to commute to college for a few months. The decision was made by the college administration on the basis of distance from the school. What upset this young woman was that some of the future commuters live miles from public transportation facilities, while some of the girls assigned to existing dormitory rooms live a block from the subway. Something in this seemed absurd, nonsensical to her. I agreed. I then suggested that it would seem fairly simple to hold a meeting of all the girls affected by this decision. They all live within five miles of the college, after all. The problem could be presented, points of view brought up, and an attempt could be made to reach a group consensus. Certainly some girls would have more compelling reasons for wanting to move into a dormitory than others. When I suggested this group approach, the girl and her parents thought it was a fascinating and creative idea, but no one from the college had thought of evolving a group consensus. What is lacking is any tradition or habit of older and younger people working together *as equals* to solve a group problem. The middle-aged voice is heard, the young voice ignored. The establishment's values prevail.

Some psychiatrists are beginning to realize that psychiatry is *another* establishment. When a patient enters therapy, he has no influence over the rules of the game. He must arrive on time or pay anyway, talk about his feelings without expecting his therapist ever to reveal his own; in short he must accept a dependent and powerless role in exchange for the hope of relief. Some patients, particularly the conventional middle-aged, accept these conditions; to today's radical or "alienated" youth, they are intolerable. The less influence an adolescent has over his therapy, the more likely he is to drop out. The author of *The Hippies' Handbook* comments that almost all "hippies" he talked to have attempted psychotherapy somewhere, but almost all felt they were not understood and not helped. They quit. The battle over who will make the rules by which life is lived is a fact of life in psychotherapy. This makes effective psychotherapy harder for young people to find. Even while most psychotherapists understand how parents' own problems and limitations have disturbed their children as they grew up, they find it hard to see how they themselves resemble those same parents in their need to control how the children will live and develop.

Recently I talked to a couple of professionals who work in a large private psychiatric clinic. This psychiatrist and psychologist have been trained to see how the unconscious needs and tensions of parents tend to color the way they deal with their teen-age children. In one case, the psychiatrist told me of a mother who never expressed concern over her son's behavior no matter what he did, while the father gave the boy an example of impulsive, inconsistent behavior, unaware of the boy's imitation of his pattern. When the parents took a long vacation at a crucial time, the boy dropped out of school. The psychiatrist found himself angry at the parents, beginning to realize how much he himself wanted the boy to stay in school. The parents had sabotaged *his* goals for the boy. I asked, "Does the boy himself want to stay in school?" The psychiatrist replied, "But isn't it self-evident that staying in school is *good* for the boy?" No. Not unless the boy himself can see what school can do for him, not unless he wants something school has to offer. It was significant that the psychiatrist could not say that he had been angry at the parents for undermining what their son felt he needed; they had undermined what the psychiatrist wanted for the boy. With all goodwill and years of training, it seems to me that many psychiatrists, psychologists, and social workers fall unwittingly into this trap, where they are joined by teachers, principals, guidance counselors, youth workers, judges, police, and probation officers. Knowing what kind of life is good for us does not mean we know what is good for another. One patient must find out what kind of life he wants for himself. We can help him, advise him, show him our example. That is what this book is about. But be it ever so tempting, we must not get into the driver's seat. For one, going back to school is progress. For another, it is copping out.

Within a family or within a school, the question of decision-making, of authority becomes more complex. Three years after the School started, I complained to an old friend about the intensity of involvement required from me to direct the School. I told her how much more involved I felt with the kids I know in the School than those I know through individual therapy alone, and how hard I felt it was to consider everyone's needs and feelings all the time. Here were seventy people and as the director, I had to be sensitive to them, and that meant no "dead" time for me around the School. Almost every moment called for involvement at a depth that tired me as much as it delighted me. Above all, I complained that when I happened to be away for even a few days things tended to get fouled up. People got upset, plans miscarried, and I had to get things back in shape on my return. "What did you expect?" she asked. "If you want a circus, you must have an elephant!"

That got me thinking about the structure of the School. I had set it up at first as an extension of my private practice, and I was running it the way my father ran his optometry shop trying to make every decision or at least to know about every one and encouraging everyone to need me. In fact more than once it was pointed out to me that I tended to make flimsy arrangements for management of the School during my occasional absences, because I seemed to enjoy being needed, being in the center of things. I realized that I was doing just that. I would prefer to think of myself as a benevolent ruler rather than an elephant, but however it comes out, I was Big Daddy to the School. For awhile I have borne the nickname "Supershrink"—once a student even presented me with a hand-made Supershrink medal, a cartoon version of the Distinguished Service award, to hang on a ribbon around my neck.

As a result of these awarenesses, I started looking at the way other schools and youth programs are administered. I found that the most "democratic" setups—drop-in centers and free schools—are run by consensus. Everybody decided everything. If nothing is decided, nothing is done. Some of our students at the School are refugees from such places where, as one girl put it, "nothing ever happens. You go there and they say, 'Should we have a pottery class today?' and no one feels like it, so there's no class. You light up a joint and sit around!" Some schools thus operated have died, and others have come to the realization that decisions must be made, and something must happen, or you have chaos: you lose your students and maybe play host to the narcotics squad. Yet the other horn of the dilemma is seen in the exaggerated example of the typical suburban high school, where decisions are made in advance, and efficiently, things get done but all unrelated to the needs and wants of the students, often driving them toward alienation. Sometimes someone realizes this and sometimes something is done about it. In our local high school, when an administrative advisory board was being formed, the last ones thought of to be members were the students. First the career administrators, then teachers, much later a few parents and then—oops, we need a couple of sample students. A psychiatrist friend of mine who has worked in federal and state drug rehabilitation programs has told me of a special kind of listening administrators use when dealing with selected adolescents who are admitted to the ruling councils of institutions. Their words are heard, but not with the same importance of those of adults. They are not taken seriously. And often if they protest that they are being effectively ignored, administrators get angry, feeling, "After all we've done for you, you're not satisfied!" The *real* power remains in the hands of the adults.

Somewhere in between these extremes lies our School, neither a pure democracy nor a dictatorship. Our administration is a kind of "benevolent empire." From solo leadership by myself, we now have added two associate directors, one a psychiatrist. Lois is a consultant to the directors. Psychodrama leaders and another psychiatrist are now the group leaders for over half our students, not me alone anymore. Ideas for future policies and changes tend to be brought up by students in group therapy sessions, which are also used to discuss important School business. There are now monthly staff meetings where teachers bring up their ideas about how things are going and how they feel things should go. And then there are endless discussions into the wee hours of the night. Every plan, decision, issue, ends up discussed by the entire group, where it can be amended, dropped, changed, or affirmed. So my own personal role of elephant or emperor has been diluted, and my personal responsibilities are now shared.

Actually what we have is a kind of family administrative structure, where parents are in charge, but highly sensitive to the feelings of the staff and the kids. I was interested to read a recent article in the *Saturday Review*, evaluating some of the "best" private schools in New England. The writer discovered that the best schools tend to emerge from the character of their headmaster and their style of operation is basically his style. When the headmaster changes, the policies may remain the same, but the school changes at its core. When I took one of my sons to visit Windsor Mountain School (one of the ones discussed in *SRL*), I was amused to see the headmaster's door burst open no less than every thirty seconds as he tried to talk to us. Every time it was an excited student who had something he *had* to talk to Heinz about, always something urgent. Of course, that's my life at the School. If I want uninterrupted time with someone, we must hide. And no matter how available one is, one can never be quite available *enough* for adolescents. In the light of earlier chapters about the unavailability of many parents, particularly fathers, it is no surprise that an administrative model resembling an *ideal* family works; such a model may be the best, because it satisfies the needs of adolescents:

> To have decisions made by more experienced adults, if their own opinions are really heard and if they are allowed to have real influence upon the decisions of adults.
>
> To have adult decision-making models with whom they can identify as they learn to make their own decisions.

# 13 › Families I: The Clash of Values

EVERY ONE OF THE young people I described in Chapter 5 came to the School for help because they could find no way to go forward into a full life. Distrustful, angry, and hurt, these kids saw the whole world in the image of the homes they were brought up in. And everyone is prepared to admit that the adolescent who has spent his childhood in a really disturbed family will deal with the world in the style he has learned at home. So Brad and Betsy and Patty and Wanda would need what psychiatrists call a "corrective emotional experience." If they could let themselves trust a therapist enough to reveal themselves, they might find out that you don't automatically get rejected or ignored when others get to know you. And after one experience of love and respect, the next such relationship is much easier to find. As one young girl put it: "I don't talk to people because it's better if they don't know me and don't know what to expect. Once they expect something from me, they'll be disappointed in me. If you are no good, you shouldn't let people see it." This girl got along well on the fringe of the group, never speaking, but when she was finally noticed, she wanted to flee. Overwhelmingly wanting love, she pulled away because she feared no one would love her. And for kids like herself and Brad and Betsy and Patty the prescription for therapy is clear—a new relationship, a new and different and more honest emotional experience.

But not all of these kids at our School come from particularly "sick" homes. I could explore deeply into the lives of Chester's and Chris's and Vic's parents, and I could, as a trained psychiatrist, find some conflicts and dissatisfactions which affected the lives of the children as they grew. But the point is that if you probe deeply enough, *every* family has weaknesses. And today the tide of adolescent disturbances is running high among the largest privileged group the world has ever known—the American middle class. I am only one individual, but no less than twice a week I have been asked to see a teen-ager who has run away from what appears to be a good home. And after investigation it is turning out more and more often that the home is not "evil"; the rebellion is more and more often against the culture the parents represent, not just against the parents themselves.

Looking over the cases in which the home and parents are *not* rejecting, overly rigid, punitive or neglectful, what can we find to account for the growing alienation of so many bright and creative young people from their parents' way of life? Chester said it, and Chris and Vic and almost every adolescent who runs away from a "good" middle-class home says it. "My parents and I are not close—we don't communicate."

What do the kids mean when they say this? They mean that their parents give them instructions about cleaning your room, doing the dishes, borrowing the car. They give you your allowance, look at your report card, ask you if you have done your homework, tell you not to smoke dope. But rarely or never do they talk with you about what is really important to you or to them—no sessions about what is to be gotten from work in a field that fascinates you, how it feels to love someone, what success and failure mean, what part sex plays in the life of a mature adult, and so on. In short, all the things parents think about by themselves and rarely share with anyone are the things kids need to hear about openly. In this complex confusing society, we adults are forced to work out our own ideas about what life is all about. These ideas we *must* share with our adolescents, even if we have doubts and are in no way sure what we feel. Our kids need desperately to meet and know us as *people*, not only as parents.

As I study the families of many of my young "alienated" patients, I keep hearing an insistent voice inside myself: "But some of these families are pretty solid! They are as good as any nuclear family. The parents have stuck together, they care for each other. Father cares about his work and does well at it. Mother cares about the home and kids and does well at that. There are values expressed. There is responsibility, concern, caring, and morality. We may expect a little "adolescent rebellion," okay, but why heroin, homosexual prostitution, alcoholism? And above all, why can't these young people from the good middle-class families find some sort of a life with meaning and commitment? We no longer have the Freud-given right to find psychopathology in the families of all deeply disturbed adolescents. We must somehow account for these dangerous disturbances of adolescence by looking beyond the problems of the nuclear middle-class family.

Erik Erikson made us aware of the tremendous role of culture in shaping the lives of children. He pointed out that cultures pass their values and beliefs through to the children, who must learn and espouse these values in order to ensure cultural continuity. Cultures in which older people are very sure they are living "correctly" are becoming rare these days. But in various parts of the earth there are still remote places, untouched by TV and rock music, money and electronic communication, and jet planes, where the elders pass on rules and judgments with absolute conviction. I described one such culture at the beginning of this book. In these societies, everyone feels little doubt over what is right or what do we do now. Even killing, headhunting, and cannibalism are performed in such societies without much conflict because the traditional values are strong and unquestioned. In such cultures there is great support and encouragement for the young person who acts according to tradition. He is likely to do what grandparents and parents advise. Their advice comes from the village elders whose advice came from *their* parents, etc. There is a *right* and a *wrong*. Margaret Mead calls such simpler cultures "postcognitive"—everyone learns from the elders. Bruno Bettelheim has described a variation of this situation in *Children of the Dream,* in which he studies the effects of the culture of an Israeli kibbutz upon the children. He finds *certainty* in that subculture, and that helps the children know what is expected of them.

The American middle class is quite a different sort of culture. The effect of ever more rapid changes in our society over the last half-century has been to confuse everybody as to what's right and what's wrong, if there *is* a right or wrong.

Even the most alienated adolescents I have known do not accuse their parents of believing in *nothing*. But they find themselves in 1973 unable to believe in what their parents apparently hold dear. The great debate with their parents' values goes more or less as follows:

#### OBEY THE LAWS

*Parents*: "A community must live in an orderly way under law. If a law is unreasonable, work within the law to change the law. Wait till you can vote, elect representatives pledged to change the laws. Take around petitions, and work for legitimate political candidates."

*A Harvard Sophomore*: "I haven't noticed the black people in America got very far by waiting for parliamentary procedures. Even Martin Luther King said if the black people waited for the civil rights laws to be acted on, it would take another hundred years. You have to show the people in control that you will take what you want if they don't let you have it.

"In the riot we had at Harvard over the ROTC issue, I

didn't particularly feel that the university should have completely banned the ROTC program from the campus. Just making it an elective course without credit was good enough. But, it's lousy to have to wait and hope for the administration to get the message and make changes. When they don't seem to see how the students feel, we can only demonstrate—*they* have the power. Then when we demonstrate, they suspend us and take away our scholarships. That's punishment for political action! And we wouldn't have had to demonstrate if we had some *voting* power on administrative boards.

"You don't get any place obeying the laws: if they are stupid, ignore them. Threats to law and order *work*—that's what they found out in Birmingham and Watts and it should work in colleges too."

**A *fifteen-year-old high school student***: "This marijuana law is absurd! Imagine a felony to smoke grass! Everyone who tries it knows it just makes you feel good. You don't even get hung over afterwards! And my parents stand around with their bourbon on the rocks and beer, telling me that getting high on grass will make an addict of me!

"The marijuana law isn't even based on real research results. Anyone who reads the papers can see that just as many experts think it's harmless as the other way. Adults make these laws to keep us in line with what they believe. They don't even know what it's all about. I even tried to turn my parents on for free, and they won't even try smoking grass, but they still condemn it!"

**A *sixteen-year-old girl***: "I've had an active sex life since last year. Sex is a pleasure to me. I don't feel it should be kept for the guy you finally marry, though it's better with someone you love. Anyway, I want to avoid having babies. I know I'm too young and unsettled to be a mother.

"Why won't they let me have birth control pills? It's just the grown-ups saying they think what I'm doing is wrong, and pregnancy would be their way of punishing me. As a matter of fact, I'm pretty sure I'm getting more pleasure from sex than my mother is. I don't plan to stop; I'll just use whatever protection I can get!"

## EDUCATION IS VITAL

*Parents*: "Get a good education so you can get a good job: People who are not trained will end up doing menial work or out of a job. Since money is so important, everyone needs to have a way of making money to support himself and his family. We really had to struggle during the Depression to survive and get ahead. It taught us the value of a dollar. These kids just spend whatever they can get on whatever pleases them at the time. Work comes first—that is, after education. But they both come *before* pleasure!"

*A twenty-three-year-old drug dealer*: "My father must have enjoyed his work, I guess. Anyway, he went to work early, came home late, and brought a lot of work home with him. The shadow of his work hung over our lives. Every day the stock market reports. And the few times we got away together he still got the paper, read about the stocks, and if something went down that day, it spoiled his vacation! I got the idea that if responsible work was like that, I'd find some other way to live.

"In high school it's all set up to make you be like your father. The college-prep curriculum for the bright kids, the vocational stuff for the hoods. In between you're *nobody*. Creative stuff like art, crafts, music, and writing are all electives for low credit. And the advisors always push you into the college stuff. 'To get a good job!' But I don't know anyone in a 'good job' who looks *happy*! Why do it if it makes you a tired-out, worried robot like my father?"

## RELIGION IS NECESSARY

*Parents (a diminishing number of them)*: "We have always gone to church. Not regularly, but off and on—either to her church or mine. It doesn't make much difference which one, but it was always hard to get the kids to go. They don't like to sit still and keep quiet that long, but we know it's good for them. Sometimes we have to make them go. And it's hard to keep that up. So lately we have given up taking the older ones if they object.

"But in these times you need something to believe in. With all this war and suffering, it's good to think about your fellow man, at least on Sunday. It puts you back in perspective."

A *twenty-two-year-old drug dealer*: "I never felt close to my parents. They sometimes went to church and took me, on holidays mostly. I didn't like getting dressed up, or sitting there quietly for two hours. Worst of all, the vibrations were wrong. My parents took it as an *obligation*, not as a pleasure. The minister was a very tense guy—he didn't seem to be feeling good about it, either. I used to wish I was an orthodox Jew or a black kid, so I could sing and shout in church and feel something other than bored and irritated. The first two times I took acid were bummers. I had to look at how depressed and angry I was inside myself. That was when I was about eighteen. But one Sunday out in the woods I took my third trip. And that's when I realized what religion *really* is. It seemed the woods and the sun and I were part of one huge *unity*, that everything is part of one thing, and that there is a design and purpose to life. I'll always be glad I took that trip. Whatever the risks might be, it was worth it to me."

A *sixteen-year-old high school dropout*: "I am trying to learn how to meditate. Partly to get over the need for drugs, I sometimes start to think about tripping when I have lots of free time. It's a kind of easy way to meditate, to get a religious or mystical experience. Even though it's sometimes very beautiful, I have begun to feel lately that it would be more *real* to be able to reach that state of mind *myself* without any drugs. That would mean my head was in really good shape. So I've been studying yoga, zen, and transcendental meditation. Of course, the problem is that when you get your mind quiet, you start seeing *yourself*. And for me, that's often kind of bad. I don't think much of myself. But I get closer to a feeling of where it's really at when I meditate than I ever did in church."

MATURITY IS ACCEPTING RESPONSIBILITY

*Parents*: "*Responsible* people should run things. Before anyone should be in charge of a company, or a school or a family, he should be grown up. A leader should have training and experience and *maturity*. That is, he should think of the good of his government or firm or family first and foremost. He should be steady and *reliable*, not impulsive and changeable."
*A fifty-year-old woman (parent and school teacher) at a conference on youth problems*: "You kids don't realize that life is a series of responsibilities, and that many or most of them can often be *boring*, irritating, and hard. I have a *contract* with my husband and children. I *cook* for them, do their laundry, shopping, cleaning. I go to work every day to augment my husband's income. And a lot of this is *not* fun, *not* pleasure. But I do it all because I am responsible to them! Because they *count* on me to do it all, even though I don't enjoy a lot of it!"

At this point a dozen high school students at the conference burst into loud laughter. The lady was very annoyed with this disrespectful interruption. In the discussion that followed, the students expressed this point of view:

*Students*: "Maybe if you feel that so much of life is just boring responsibility, you shouldn't have taken all of that on. When our parents give us that martyred line about how *hard* it all is, we get angry. *We* didn't ask them to do it. No one should do much of anything he doesn't *like* to do. Life is to *enjoy* and to get with, not to suffer through. If your life fills up with draggy obligations, reevaluate it and change it so you get more joy every day. Figure out what you'd *like* to be doing, and do it. You'll find that some of what you'll do is for others. Trust yourself!"

I could give many more examples of the issues on which parents' values and those of a growing number of adolescents are opposed. But by now certain core differences are clear. These kids want life to be *enjoyable,* and they don't want to wait till they are their parents' age to enjoy it. In any case these young people don't see their parents and their parents' peers enjoying life. More precisely, they don't see these older people living up to their human potential for self-actualization. In Maslow's terms, these young people want life to be more of a peak experience all the way—a participation in love, nature, the body, faith, work, and creativity. They have been "turned on" to what took many of their parents a lifetime to find out—that a state of exaltation can and should be part of life—*everyday* life. What is sad is that once they have made this vital discovery, most of these kids don't know how to create this kind of life on their own and without psychedelic drugs, which do in fact expose them to exactly this state of being—temporarily.

Faced by clashes of basic values, kids and parents seem to avoid battles by pulling apart, not expecting to talk honestly with each other about anything of importance. The invasion of homes by mass media makes parent-child interaction even more difficult to arrange. If the figures quoted in Chapter 11 are any indication, it seems that the middle-class suburban adolescents spend twenty-four times as many minutes watching TV as they do discussing anything with their parents, and from ten to twenty times again as much time exposed to other mass media. The parent-child interaction seems not to be getting prime time.

In following this up, I ran into some interesting comments by Nicholas Johnson, a Federal Communications Commissioner, in the *Television Quarterly*, Vol. VIII, Number 1 (1969). Johnson says:

"There are 60 million homes in the United States and over 95 percent of them are equipped with a television set. (More than 25 percent have two or more sets.) In the average home (the *average* home) the set is turned on some five hours and forty-five minutes a day. The average male viewer, between his second and sixty-fifth year, will watch television for over 3000 entire days—roughly nine full years of his life. During the average weekday winter evening nearly half of the American people are to be found silently seated with fixed gaze upon a phosphorescent screen, experiencing the sensation of its radiation upon the retina of the eye."

If Johnson's comments seem exaggerated, look back at the case histories I have presented, and find in almost every one the disturbing theme of little closeness between parent and child in these homes:

**Patty**: "If [my father] talks to me for ten minutes when I'm depressed, he acts like he should be elected father of the year!"
**Chester's father**: "I gave up trying to be a father to him . . . now that he's nineteen. I don't understand him. . . . I'd like to help him, but I can't see how to do it!"
**Chris**: "My father . . . was going up the ladder in his business so fast he couldn't spare the time for us. . . . I never got to talk to him. My mother . . . didn't go in much for taking care of us herself."
**Vic**: "My father . . . never told me anything about his life as a young man. We never could communicate anyway. Somehow we never knew each other . . . as people, I mean."

I believe that Johnson and Bandura and Hayakawa and others are onto something—that the mass media have introduced a new element of major proportions into the lives of American families; television has taken over the American living room and usurped the prime time which might have been used for *active* interrelating of parents and children and turned these thousands of hours into electronic baby-sitting for all ages. If the kids fight, daddy feels he should get up and referee. He teaches the kids conciliation techniques that are neither better nor worse than daddy is, but whether the kids learn or not from daddy's effectiveness or ineffectiveness at fight settling, they do learn about *Daddy*. What they learn is *real*. In front of the TV screen they are passive, daddy doesn't have to do anything, and they don't *relate*. And in the blessed family where all ages watch the baseball game every Sunday afternoon, are they relating with each other? What are the kids finding out about how real people handle real situations?

I have like most parents long known that TV was exposing my own children to a biased view of life. But a lifetime subscription to *Mad* magazine does not completely counteract this pop-culture spreader in the living room. And seeing to it that your children have lots of time with their parents and plenty of active experiences through which to master skills and learn to face difficult tasks is a lifelong hard administrative job for any parent. Whatever its failings, watching TV is *easier*. And people tend to do what is easy.

Recently I read an excerpt from an essay by Ernest Van den Haag ("Of Happiness and Despair We Have No Measure," excerpted in *Mass Media and Mass Man*, edited by Alan Costy). After quoting Henry David Thoreau, "The mass of men lead lives of quiet desperation . . . a stereotyped but unconscious despair is concealed even under what are called the games and amusements of mankind," Van den Haag adds, "Despair, we find, is no longer quiet. Popular culture tries to exorcise it with much clanging and banging. Perhaps it takes more noise to drone it out. Perhaps we are less willing to face it. But whether wrapped in popular culture, we are less happy than our quieter ancestors, or the natives of Bali, must remain an open question despite all romanticizing." (Nor do we have a feasible alternative to popular culture. Besides, a proposal for "the mass of men" would be unlikely to affect the substance of popular culture, and counsel to individuals must be individual.)

A relationship between a son and his father or a daughter and her mother is individual. It is not composed of generalities, of mass assumptions. A main goal of any relationship between *individuals* is the communication of how the individuals feel about each other, and in the case of parent and child, some lessons of life learned by *this* parent taught to *this* child and vice versa. No person on earth can replace *this* parent for *this* child. When a parent for any reason abdicates "prime time" and allows his child's life to be dominated by mass TV emanations by PR men, he abdicates to some extent the primacy of his relationship with his child. Five minutes a day is not enough time to transmit feelings about the meaning and direction of life and certainly not enough to communicate love and caring. Once there is no longer any communication between parent and child, each party tends to fill the emptiness with canned messages from his favorite mass medium.

In recent years, at least one of the mass media has come more and more to express some of the feelings of adolescents. On the jackets of rock records, you can read in the notes and the texts of songs what many young people feel about the middle-class society in which they were brought up, and from which they have "dropped out." For example, the famous song by John Lennon and Paul McCartney, "A Day in the Life":

> *About a lucky man who made the grade . . .*
> *He blew his mind out in a car*
> *He didn't notice that the light had changed . . .*

The message comes through in a large body of rock material, sometimes in the notes on the record jacket as well as in the songs. Here is an excerpt from Allen Ginsberg's notes for the Fugs (ESP disk 1028):

"It's war on all fronts. 'Breakthrough in the Grey Room' says Burroughs—he meant the Brain. 'Total Assault on the Culture' says Ed Sanders. The United States is split down the middle. On one side are everybody who make love with their eyes open, maybe smoke pot and maybe take LSD and look inside their heads to find the Self-God Walt Whitman prophesied for America. 'Fool' said the Muse, 'look in your heart and write.' Dylan goes beyond: 'Catch me disappearing in the smokerings of my mind.' I say I'm confused, I'm frightened. I don't know. Who's on the other side? People who think we are *bad*. Other side? No, let's not make it a war, we'll all be destroyed, we'll go on suffering till we die if we take the War Door. Yogis and Beatles say there is no other side— 'We can get along.' Can't we? I say we can get along. People in there think sex body loves are bad—I say make love to *them*. They need it most. We all have to be funny saints to survive. Birchites are lacklove, Republicans and Democrats too are lacklove. Communists lack love, Narco fuzz and White South governors lack love . . ."

There is a war going on. Some months ago I visited one of the battlefields. My oldest son, who is a bass guitarist in a rock group, asked me to drive him to the home of another kid who wanted to sell a bass amplifier. At the time my son had no driver's license, so I was transportation. We ended up that Sunday morning in front of a lower-middle-class home in the country. A sign advised us that the father was a contractor who did home renovations. His own home needed painting and fixing, but it was a pleasant place, set among old oaks and pines. As we entered by the kitchen door (the front door was not in use), we met the father of the family at Sunday breakfast in his undershirt. With him was another son, home on leave from the Marines, still crew-cut but growing a furlough beard. Both waved cheery hellos.

Mother was a stout friendly woman in a flowered dress who

told us that Herbie, her fifteen-year-old and seller of the bass amp, was out at a rehearsal of his rock band, but Herbie had told mother to sell it to us if we would pay 150 dollars. She led us past a giant color TV in the living room and picked one of the little tinted photographs off the TV to show us. Here in a gold frame was Herbie, but about thirteen years old and with short hair, pink tinted cheeks, blue eyes, etc.

"He has long hair now and I don't like it," said Mother, "but he won't cut it. All of his rock friends have long hair too. None of the parents like it. Some of them force them to cut it, but we don't."

Upstairs we passed a chair with a few of Mother's girdles on it. This she pushed out of the way. We also passed a GOD BLESS OUR HOME sign in a twig frame. But when we came to Herbie's tiny room under the eaves we found a different environment. "He doesn't like the striped wallpaper anymore, so he painted the room." It was electric blue. "He took down the cowboy curtains he used to love, too." Herbie's room was packed with electronic equipment—amplifiers, speakers, electric guitars. My son's eyes lit up and he started checking out the bass amp. Knowing this was going to take awhile, I looked round. On the walls were posters, of course. Herbie's gods included the Beatles, Frank Zappa and the Mothers of Invention, Bob Dylan and the Maharishi Mahesh Yogi.

Then I noticed that a record jacket had been tacked to the wall over Herbie's bed, just where he could see it as he lay on his pillow. And it was tacked up so the back side was visible—the side with the text, not the picture. And this was where I first read Allen Ginsberg's comments, the ones I just quoted. "Total assault on the culture!" Like the Gideon bible in a hotel room, *this* was the only reading material Herbie could see in the place. He had put it in the place of honor. As I read it, Mother rattled on. "I don't understand Herbie's music —what it's all about. And it's so loud! But he loves it and it keeps him busy and out of trouble!"

Ginsberg is telling Herbie: "On one side are everybody who

*Families I: The Clash of Values*

make love with their eyes open, maybe smoke pot and maybe take LSD and look inside their heads to find the Self-God Walt Whitman prophesied for America. . . . People in there think sex body loves are bad—I say make love to *them!* . . . Teenagers rise up and understand! When they scream 'Kill for Peace!' they're announcing publicly the madness of our white-haired crazy governments."

Here in this most ordinary home an ideological gulf exists— and it is not even recognized. Home renovations, the U.S. Marines, color TV, and tinted photographs versus rock music, the Fugs, Allen Ginsberg, marijuana, LSD and the self-god. Norman Vincent Peale versus Walt Whitman. "God Bless Our Home" versus "Teenagers rise up and understand!" And this war is *not* political or economic or religious. It is all of these and more. The war is over the meaning and purpose of life.

In fact, if you believe what Marshall McLuhan has to say, it looks like the clash of values between teen-agers and their parents is based upon the probability that they are actually different kinds of people. In McLuhan's terms, middle-class parents are people programmed unconsciously by being brought up in the world of reading *print*, with visual sense heightened and tactile, auditory, and other senses relatively dulled. People like this are schooled in discriminating, McLuhan says, and relate to their world by abstracting and fragmenting. As Tom Wolfe summarizes McLuhan's position (in Wolfe's *The Pump House Gang*), this emphasis on western man's visual discrimination led to "nationalism and nationalist wars (cultural fragmentation); the modern army, industrialism and bureaucracy (fragmentation of tasks); the market and price structure (economic fragmentation); individualism and the habit of privacy (fragmentation of the individual from the community)—schizophrenia and peptic ulcers (caused by the fragmentation of both intellect and action from emotion); pornography (fragmentation of sex from love); the cult of childhood (fragmentation by age);

*Somebody Knows What Is Best for You*

and a general impoverishment of man's intuitive and artistic life (because of the fragmentation of the senses)." McLuhan believed that all this changed radically when TV came in. Our eighteen-year-olds, the world's first "TV generation," are not using their minds the way their print-programmed visually oriented parents do, not at all. Young people want to *hear* and *feel* and *move*—and *together*, not alone. They have been trained by electric media, primarily TV, to recognize *patterns*, wholes, and, in Wolfe's words, "they sit baffled and bored in classrooms run by teachers who fragment knowledge into 'subjects,' disciplines, specialities, and insist on the classification of data." If it doesn't come on like *Sesame Street*, no one can get into it these days.

One night I played my favorite records for a twenty-year-old girl. Jazz, chamber music, folk performances—none of it moved her at all. "Don't think I don't appreciate the skill of Brubeck or Monk or Casals—I just don't like any kind of music you have to think about or really listen to. I just like the sound to be all around me and make me move!" She and her young friends don't want to *appreciate*, they want to *feel*. And they find the fragmented world of their parents unsatisfying because in it feeling is subjugated to thinking, calculating, working, and categorizing. Perhaps this is the unconscious basis of the values clash between parent and child.

So we find the American middle-class child watching television over two hours a day, enjoying deep involvement with his parents for less than five minutes a day, and as he reaches adolescence filling his out-of-school time listening to the pop and rock music he can hear on his stereo set and portable radio anytime he feels like flipping a switch. To what extent he actually adopts Rowan and Martin or Alexander Mundy (or other TV "personalities") as substitute "identification figures" I don't know. But he is getting from the content and the form of the new mass media messages which lead him to doubt the validity of his parents' world and the values which made it. To whatever extent TV and other media like radio and the stereo record player have changed the sensory absorption patterns of our young people, they have made them refractory to the messages they are receiving from their parents. A real cultural discontinuity has developed between the middle-class parent and his children; the kids are no longer getting Dad's message. They no longer want Daddy and Mom's kind of life to live, because they are living in a different world now. The mass media remind us all of this unchangeable fact every minute of every day.

# 14 › Families II: The Declaration of Personhood

TWENTY YEARS AGO Erik Erikson wrote *Childhood and Society*. In it he gave us a vital concept—that a main task for the adolescent is the development of an identity, a sense of what you are in relation to your world. When you take into account your inherited gifts and deficiencies, the personality you have developed as a result of the preadolescent stages of your development and the demands of your culture, you work out some sort of life for yourself. The life you work out tells you who you are.

In Erikson's terms, the formation of an identity in middle and late adolescence is a "normative crisis," that is, everybody goes through this time of decision. Confusion is absolutely characteristic of adolescence in a confused society. Some anthropologists like Margaret Mead have noticed that in simpler societies adolescence seems much easier—children develop more smoothly into the sort of people they will be. But in middle-class America the conflicting demands for adolescents to train themselves to fit into very complex roles in society make identity formation much more difficult. Though puberty in America comes at age ten or eleven now, the society still expects no "serious" sexual life until boys have found a career and girls are ready to become wives and mothers. And we live in an age of specialization; psychoanalysts receiving their admission to membership in psychoanalytic institutes are about forty years old when they are finally permitted to practice their specialty. It takes longer and longer to complete your training in all branches of medicine, law, architecture, engineering, computer technology. We are becoming a society where *every* self-respecting middle-class child is told he is underachieving if he does *not* contemplate going at least to college, and probably some graduate school as well.

When I was fifteen I fell in love with Sheila. We met in dark corners and under stairways in high school, kissed and caressed each other every moment we could. On weekend nights I took the hour-long street car ride to her house, took her to a movie or somewhere long enough for her parents to go to sleep, brought her home and spent hours making love to her on her living room couch. This was 1943 and making love at fifteen meant all but the last inch or two. Then the hour-long trolley ride home in the snow. And as I came up the snowy street at 4 A.M. I saw my parents' light snap off. As I crept up the stairs, I heard my mother say to my father, "Al, go in there and talk to him. Tell him he can't do this to us." Then I hurried to bed and pretended to be asleep. My father came wearily into my room in his undershorts, sat down heavily on my bed and said nothing. What would happen? I was scared but I could feel him struggling over the issue. Finally he said quietly "Shep? Shep, are you awake?" "Yes," I said. Then a long silence. "Did you have a good time?" "Yes," I said. "Go to sleep." And he left.

But that didn't relieve my mother's mind. So she called me into her room one afternoon and told me how worried she was over my affair with Sheila. This thing was too serious for fifteen-year-olds. Too intimate. We certainly couldn't be thinking of getting married. We needed our energy for school work and for doing well enough to get into college. Not once in the discussion did she mention love or recognize the intensity of the feelings I had for Sheila. Nor did she talk about sex and its complications—pregnancy, V.D., abortions, nor the pleasures of sex either. I remember wanting to burst out,

"Leave me alone, this is the best thing in my life! I love her and she loves me!" But I had already been trained that you do not speak truthfully to Mother. My father never did, and when anyone tried she just didn't hear it. Sometimes she got depressed if you defied her. So I listened, and to my everlasting shame I did not resist. She called up Sheila's parents. I was not allowed to go out with her again.

At about that time I got the equally rebellious idea that I might prefer to go to art school rather than college. I could draw and I liked making things. My father as usual was unavailable for discussion. My mother took me somewhere for aptitude testing. To my surprise I looked like a possible architect. I had something called "good structural visualization." But my broad spectrum talents were my undoing. I was also apparently good at "helping." So I was then taken to see my mother's psychoanalyst, who overpowered me with his intelligent arguments. Artists don't make a living, they are nobody. Doctors are somebody in *society*. And then more confidentially, surely I could see how my mother was counting on me becoming a doctor, not throwing my life away. That would kill her. We both knew how fragile she was, how serious her depressions could become. Again, I bowed to authority. This was the man who had given my mother shock treatments, he was eminent in the New York Psychoanalytic Society, he was my mother's god. It took me twenty more years to realize he was another one of her puppets dominated by her through her illness and the threat of her getting worse.

Pressure to become "a professional man" was very strong from both my parents, and my mother worked very hard to see that I became a psychiatrist. Erikson has coined the phrase "psychosocial moratorium" to describe how societies grant their adolescents a period of time in which they are no longer treated as children, but are not yet expected to bear the burdens of adults. In this period of delayed responsibilities, young people can experiment with future roles and decide "what to be." Essentially the "moratorium" gives time to match future career specifications against your abilities and personality traits, to see what you would *like* to be, what life style expresses you.

In my case, there was constant pressure to pass from one stage of preprofessional training to the next *without* taking time to decide whether I really wanted to be a doctor in the first place. And despite the general validity of the concept of "psychosocial moratorium," I notice that a great many middle-class adolescents are today herded, as I was, toward non-decisions about what they will do in life, how they will live. One boy put it:

"Of course, everybody where I come from must go to college and become something respectable. If you waste time getting there, your parents worry whether 'losing a year' means you are copping out or falling apart. It's all so *competitive*—staying up with your class, getting into a class A college, getting good marks so you can get into graduate school. You just don't have time to *find* your life for yourself. It's set before you like mother's supper—all cooked and ready for you to eat. You feel guilty telling her you'd rather go out for hamburgers!"

From age sixteen on I went through precisely the same situation as these kids do, to the ridiculous point that I didn't wake up to the fact that I had the right to *decide* my own profession until halfway through my psychoanalytic training. And age thirty is a little late for an identity crisis. I had a family I was already supporting, I was a fully trained psychiatrist, I had let myself be molded to the point where really changing my life was now terribly difficult.

I had never actually *decided* consciously to become a psychoanalyst. I grew up in a family very much like the ones my adolescent patients come from. You can read about families like mine in Keniston's book *The Uncommitted*. My father was a sweet man, "never hurt anyone." He was an optometrist and had built up his own shop. He spent seven days a week and twelve hours a day examining eyes and making glasses. To see much of him, I would have had to have bad vision. But I had 20/20. It took me till I was thirteen to figure out how to get near him. I did it by spending Sundays working in his place, bottling eyeglass cleaning fluid and doing odd jobs. I found out that after all he was kind and generous, could exert no discipline, and was working himself to death. He left the raising of my sister and myself almost entirely to my mother, her mother, and a maid.

Mother was very sick. She had recurrent depressions that lasted a year or two at a time. She had suffered her first depression when I was very small, and then six years later she became depressed again. I remember her weeping in her bed, the bed table crammed with bottles of sleeping pills and other medicines. She trembled, smoked three packs of cigarettes a day. I was the oldest and the only son. Many times she told me her story: she had been the "ugly sister," the one her mother "didn't like." She had loved her father, another sweet kind passive man. His death touched off her depression when I was eleven. Her life story was one of lost hopes, unused talent. She had been good in college, but gave up a chance to go to law school in order to get married. Marriage to my father had been a disappointment. He was "sweet and devoted" but somehow not what she wanted. I must never settle for being like him. Mother was overpowering, devouring in her endless neediness. I was to be the one who could *really* understand her, and ultimately I would be the psychiatrist who would make the discoveries that would save her. I could do almost anything. I was superboy, so long as I did not try to be free of her.

Working with my father on Sundays, I discovered he was a man of stature when he was not at home. At his office he was *somebody*, the boss. I learned Yiddish so we could enjoy the Yiddish theater together; I prodded him to take me there, and that is how we met each other as adults. This was the old-country Yiddish "crude" side of him that my mother couldn't accept, and above all she did not want me to be like that. I was to be a brilliant psychiatrist, an intellectual, a famous man.

I went through college and medical school the way kids today go through third grade. Not sure of what I wanted, not sure who I was, I stuck to the path that would lead to psychiatry and psychoanalysis. The identity crisis finally came at the psychoanalytic institute.

The people there were all my mother ever wanted me to be. They were brilliant, intellectual, learned. We studied Freud with Talmudic exactness. I felt trapped. My reactions to my psychoanalytic instructors were bound to be critical, and they were. In addition, there was the fact that at the time I studied there the institute was a dogmatic school. Seminars tended to refer endlessly back to Freud's basic papers. Most of the teaching was lifeless and I felt oppressed there. Many of my classmates griped about this too, but nobody objected overtly. A Harvard student strike poster of 1969 says "Strike because your classes are a bore . . . Strike because they are squeezing the life out of you." If I had gone on strike from the institute, my banner would have said the same. But in those days the establishment had to be *right*; they held your future in their hands, your graduation, and your accreditation as an analyst.

I had five years of personal psychoanalysis. My first psychoanalyst was handsome, elegant, and eminent. I never felt close to him. He said very little; the Boston style of psychoanalysis is perhaps the most conservative style in the world. It seemed interminable to me. By now my mother had died suddenly after a struggle to dominate my marriage, and I was suffering with guilt. I was depressed and very angry and felt unable to steer my own life. The driver was suddenly gone, and I, who had been wanting to drive, was not sure I could do it. At this point my analyst had to leave the area for awhile—a divorce and remarriage problem came up in his life.

To cope with that event and my depression over my mother's death, I went to another analyst, a pleasant man I found less austere than the first. We made very slow progress for another two years.

One critical incident that sticks in my mind concerns the

time when my second analyst told me he was moving his office from a dingy Boston brownstone to the basement of his suburban home. I remember coming into the new place and feeling a strong feeling about it. A tiny entryway, waiting room, a small bathroom, and an office had been constructed there. I remember the sudden thought, "This place is completely phony." Walls made of that plywood veneer that looks like birch, floor of vinyl tile over concrete, ceiling of soundproofing tile—no windows; an air conditioner stuck through the wall. The furniture was smooth, modern, anonymous. There was no more of this man visible in his new office than in his manner; the office was also a front, like the analytic manner.

I am fully aware as I write these words that anonymity is a *technique* in traditional psychoanalysis. It was taught to me as part of *listening* to the patient. The idea is to give the patient as little as possible upon which to form concrete ideas about the analyst. The reasoning goes that if he knows next to nothing about the analyst he will construct his own fantasies about him. These fantasies must come from his own past, usually his relationship with his parents, and can be analyzed as such.

All this would be impressive if patients were not always picking up even the tiniest cues as to the analyst's personality despite all his attempts to be "neutral." In my own case, one day the subject of my folksinging career came up. I had done this for years, since I was fourteen. I had radio programs and had cut five record albums. Frequently my psychiatric patients would come to my concerts or buy my records and tell me what they felt about this side of my life. I had become used to dealing with these reactions and tracing their roots back to the patients' own needs and fantasies. I was therefore amazed to hear my analyst break his normal silence to tell me that he felt being a "public performer" was not consistent with being a psychoanalyst. Patients would learn about my fantasies and feelings from my choice of songs and how I sang them,

*Families II: The Declaration of Personhood*

thus they would know too much about me. Now, perhaps if I sang under another name . . .

I felt that I was being told that I could not pursue a career in psychoanalysis and still feel free to use the creative channel of singing. This session had a disastrous effect on my singing. For a long time I stopped performing, and I missed it. Conflict had entered this area. I am not saying that I was unwilling to understand the "neurotic roots" of the singing. I had used it to please my mother, to woo her. But we had been over that ground in the analysis. What happened now between us felt like a parental edict:

*Analyst*: "To get my approval you must become anonymous like me."
*Myself*: (first) "I can't do it." (later) "*I won't* do it."

Encounters like this made me feel I was not the sort of man who could enjoy being a psychoanalyst, at least not like either of my own psychoanalysts and most of my classmates at the institute. I resigned.

Of course, the parallel between my leaving the institute and many of my young patients leaving school and colleges is obvious. I was trying to work out serious personal problems and thus to find *myself*. The school did not help me to find *myself*; it seemed to me to offer a stereotyped role which I could either accept or get out. Faced with that impossible choice, I resigned from the institute. I kept on singing. The institute never asked the reasons for my resignation.

Many a creative youth, looking for help, finds a therapist who cannot see his creative uniqueness. More than half of the kids I talk to these days have tried therapy already and failed to find someone who understood. Of course, most psychiatrists, psychologists, and social workers understand the problems of the disturbed family, but not many are yet attuned to the specialness of creative personalities. It is a very poor painting teacher who would tell a student what to paint or how to paint it, yet the atmosphere of pressure towards "normal" (typical, conventional) behavior is still heavy on young people seeking help. A therapist has the enormous advantage of his own life experience, which is often relevant to an adolescent's life problems and choices. This he should share with his patient, not withhold. But he does not, cannot fully understand the dilemma of growing up *today* for *this* adolescent. He is not growing up *today*. His today is not the same as his patient's. And the creative young are pioneers, who will develop new life styles. If psychotherapists press them toward the older, more conventional life styles, they will abandon therapy. This is tragic because of all the real help that could be found in imaginative therapy—help now lost to them because once burned, they are likely to put down therapy as useless and never return. I am sure that my experience with psychoanalysis made me receptive to the complaints of creative kids whose therapy experiences were like mine. Unfortunately, such experiences are all too common.

My experience with the psychoanalytic institute has also given me much more respect for adults who have broken out of the molds prepared for them by parents and school and society. People who have found themselves, established their own life styles, are much more convincing as teachers and guides for adolescents because they are examples of the realness the kids are trying to discover in themselves. This kind of authenticity has become one of the major criteria for selections of teachers for the School We Have.

When you compare the quality of being that is radiated by these realized and real people with that projected by the parents of many of my young patients, there is an enormous and vital difference. When anyone is deeply into his own becoming, he wants others to live real lives as well. When his friends or his children can't get into some style that feels good to them, this person feels their despair, advises them, and guides them if he can. Feeling satisfied and full of his own life, he wants others to be filled with theirs. But the feeling of so many of the parents of the kids who come to our School is very different. They operate with fear and criticism. Don't fall in love at fifteen, don't want to be an artist, don't smoke pot, don't have sex so young, don't waste energy on rock guitar that should go into better marks for college. And when I interview parents as part of the psychotherapy process for every one of my young patients, I am over and over again struck by the vibrations of dissatisfaction that these parents project. Their lives have disappointed them, turned somehow to ashes. Whatever the dreams were when they were teenagers, they are not going to be realized. After years of hope, excitement, and pleasure, they have now come to be mere custodians. Theirs is a world of properties, mortgages, insurance policies, of the welfare of children and pets and maids and the increasing costs of school buildings, into which they push their children to be taught that real life has little pleasure. You don't have to read Leonard's *Education And Ecstasy* to know what joyless tombs the schools are—you went to a few of them yourself. How many of your teachers can you remember as really joyous people? Parents who have given up their dreams of pleasure and freedom are almost never able to let their children keep intact those same dreams. You can't give your child a drink from your empty cup. Your game becomes how to get him to give you a drink from his.

So over and over again the complaint from parents about their adolescents' behavior is that they have lost control, lost influence over the child's ways. And they point to evidence of "irresponsibility" to show the child that he should listen to their directions, that if he does not follow their advice he will get into really *serious* trouble.

I am thinking of one situation where a daughter of sixteen fell deeply in love with a twenty-year-old boy. Her parents were concerned about the intensity of the relationship and they tried to limit it to dates of weekends, home by midnight, never sleeping over at anyone's house. Then the father got transferred to a new job four hundred miles away. Nancy, the daughter, didn't want to move. But the parents felt that she needed to be with them, needed the supervision. So she had to go. From that day on she no longer lived with her parents; her whole spirit remained with her man. She felt her parents as jailers and treated them as such. In this case there had been very early problems between mother and daughter that left Nancy with a deep sense of worthlessness and a tendency to feel guilty about wanting to be free. If she stood up for her wishes, her parents would show her: "You are destroying us!" Then Nancy would feel guilty, repress the guilt and turn her freedom movement against herself, as a punishment. So she would visit her lover for a weekend, come home with a cold, miss a few days of school. Her father, spokesman for her mother, would then say, "See, you can't be on your own! Every time you try it you prove you are irresponsible, you are a baby!" No amount of incisive interpretations during family therapy sessions could make these parents see that they were making Nancy into that helpless irresponsible baby, undermining her faith in herself.

Why should this mother do this to Nancy? I will probably never know why she could not give Nancy real love and strength back at the beginning. This mother has repeatedly appeared to agree with my advice, then gotten her husband to reverse it and try fruitlessly to "put their foot down." The effect is to choke off Nancy's relationship with her parents still further. As a result, family therapy in this case is not going to work. Somewhere inside, this mother herself cannot love, and thus she can't bear the intensity of Nancy's love affair, her devotion to Jimmy. She can't talk to Nancy about the joys and sorrows of love, only the sorrows. She can't give Nancy the benefit of her own love experience, but can only communicate what Nancy already knows: "My mother can't love! So she can't help me love." The love is not seen by the mother as premature or bound to end or "puppy-love dependent"—it is seen as *not love*. Mother simply cannot let Nancy love a man. Nancy must love, it is in her nature, in her womanhood.

What should these parents do? I would suggest they let

Nancy work out a way to get a job and a place to stay near Jimmy for the summer, so she can find out where the relationship is going and also learn the essentials of independent living. To be able to live like an adult carries the responsibilities of an adult. But these parents, playing on Nancy's anger and guilt, are provoking her to self-destruction. She will probably run away, maybe come back pregnant. My fear for her is that by running away and openly defying her parents her self-doubt and guilt will make her ruin the relationship with Jimmy, a setback she will take long to get over.

In working with kids individually, I always work with their parents in various ways:

*Crisis.* When urgent issues arise, a family meeting (or several) is called with me as referee. We try to understand how adolescent and parents are feeling about each other and work out agreements on behavior and mutual obligations. Sometimes this means months of conferences.

*Therapy for parents.* Singly, or as a couple, I recommend therapy for parents who seem to need it. It will be no surprise that when therapy makes a parent feel better in his own life or makes parents a better couple, a lot of the problems of the adolescents in the family seem to disappear. Certain staff members of the School have special understanding and talent for working with parents. Their feelings for parents' dilemmas are more compassionate than my own. So they work with a number of families and I keep in regular touch with them about it.

*Declaration of personhood.* There is a kind of family therapy special to adolescents, in which I find myself in the role of midwife. This young person, up 'til now thought only as a child, is now ready to be taken seriously as a person. This need has not been perceived at home, so he needs an advocate—an adult authority who takes him seriously as a person and shows his parents how to do it too. In healthy families, one or a few such sessions teaches parents how to deal with this new adult more successfully. There are some principles involved here, which I teach parents:

*Recognize that you can't control what your adolescent will do.* You can't watch him twenty-four hours a day. Your only tool is the trust he has in you, so playing detective is worse than useless, it is alienating. No searches in the bedroom drawers for drugs, pornography, or incriminating letters from juvenile dope and sex fiends. No checking up on *where* he is, or *when*, unless there is some real reason to find him. But this point is inseparable from the next—

*Share your own life experience* with your adolescent. He wants, he needs to know what you found out about life, love, career, pleasure, everything. Tell him about your deepest self whenever the opportunities arise. This will be taken as guidance, and you can trust a healthy adolescent to consider it, especially if it is offered lovingly. You cannot offer guidance as judgment or as orders, nor expect your adolescent to follow it. He decides what he will do, not you.

We have all of us come a long way from the valleys of New Guinea. There is so little we can share with our own young, now that the basic conditions of life are changing so fast and generations are two years long. No pig festivals any more to involve the spirits and energies of the elders and the young together. All responsibilities and goals must be built into our personalities now, strongly braced inside us against the pressures of the society we have built, whose prisoners we have now become. And as we lose faith in our society and the environment it has ruined for us, we are forced *inward.* Our source of strength and comfort can now only be the *self.* If you are not acquainted with yourself, you can only appear to your children to be a robot repeating the trite values and ordinances of a society that even you really don't believe in anymore.

But if we cannot share ancient rituals and festivals, we can share *ourselves.* Adolescents need to know who their parents and teachers *are*. What do you care about? What makes you happy? What makes you cry? What have you made of your life? If you can face yourself, if you *will* face yourself, they can take from you the example they must find somewhere, they will then accept your life as a kind of guide. There is nothing to be gained from criticizing what adolescents do or how they do it. Giving them advice is equally useless unless you can reveal yourself to them and to yourself as a feeling human being trying to live somehow in the H-bomb world.

Your adolescent children and students and patients will *not* accept your rules, but they will learn honesty if you reveal to them that you made *your* rules honestly.

They will not choose to live as you do, but they will learn integrity from you, if you will let them see *your* integrity.

They will make their own mistakes, but they will learn from their mistakes if you show how you have learned from yours, which means you will have to admit *your* mistakes.

Ask yourself, "Am I living the kind of life I want to live?" If the answer is no, then don't insist your adolescents live as you do. Talk together about how your life is, how it should be, and they will at least learn to avoid some of the traps you may have fallen into.

I have worked with a number of families who have been elsewhere in family therapy together. Frequently the rules were that all family members must attend every session, that all feelings must be brought up, and so on. Many adolescents find that approach too authoritarian and dictatorial and feel bound to rebel against it. In adolescence we are dealing with a phase in which the child is moving apart from the family, not closer to it. So any attempt to force the family together will cause more conflict, not less. Many a normal adolescent functions like a lodger in his own home: almost none of his feeling life is with his parents. If parents accept this as normal, bide their time, and offer really honest and open communication when there is contact, the adolescent will use that contact gratefully and this will strengthen the basic relationship with the parents. The results will be seen later, not now.

Once at the School we decided to work more intensively with the parents. Feeling that many of these issues could be understood and discussed by parents as a group and that talking about one family's problems could help another, we offered therapy groups for parents of kids attending the School. We offered expert leadership and scholarships for the needy. Of forty-five sets of parents we contacted, only four individual parents were interested. That was disappointing. We need to find some other way to get closer to more of the parents of our students. We know that progress toward freedom and "personhood" for the kids arouses conflict and sometimes strong envy among parents. If we had the resources to make an encounter-style opening-up experience available to all parents, we would. But you need to acknowledge where you are before you know where you want to go, and so far only a small minority of the parents of our kids have shown much willingness to do that.

One evening at the School our group got to talking about going home for the holidays to see your parents. Debbie and Jane and Steve were joined by Dick, a psychiatrist, in remembering how those visits feel to them. One of the kids said:

"I always see their *expectations*—the questions they ask me to find out if I'm going to become what they want me to. How's school, do I look well-dressed? If I talk about a boy, what do his parents do? Is he in college or does he have a good job? They avoid asking how I feel about him and how he feels about me. If I tell them the way I really live, that I don't work full-time, that I make love to him a lot, my mother gets upset. I think she's jealous of my freedom and my relationships with men, as well as disappointed that I'm not 'living up to my potential.' "

Another of the kids chimed in:

"I don't feel safe in sharing the treasure of my real feelings with my parents. It just happens too often that they are not going to understand. And I don't feel sure enough of myself to take that chance, yet. If they tell me I'm not living right, I resist them, but inside I wonder and get worried about myself. I want them to approve of my life the way I've set it up, not just accept it if it's the way they want me to live!"

Bill told me about how he tried to get through this barrier with his father. Bill has lived away from home for years in prep schools and college and now in music school. He has an apartment of his own and he's trying to become a musician very seriously. But he has problems with loneliness and depression, can't get close to girls comfortably, and he's been trying to come to terms with these problems at the School and in therapy with me. Bill is a serious, quiet man of twenty-two, who can't recall ever having a serious conversation with his father. His father is an engineering genius, now a millionaire, a man who's worked tremendously hard and made his fortune. But even when Bill's mother became addicted to barbiturates, even when his parents were divorced, his father never talked to him from the heart about how he felt, what he wanted—so Bill lived through these times alone, getting by without emotional support. Mother deeply sick, father deeply busy, Bill deeply alone.

Bill decided he needed to encounter his father honestly. He knew he would never do it unless he took the responsibility to make it happen. As I did when I went to work Sundays for my dad, learned Yiddish, went to him and found him where he was hiding from my family, Bill decided he would go home and stay a week with his father, try to talk to him about himself, maybe even meet each other as men. And he went home. He found his father drinking heavily, unable to keep up a conversation after two in the afternoon; all his sober hours he was at work. So there were long evenings of flat shallow conversation without meaning to Bill. He came home deeply disappointed, but prepared to see that realistically his father was not going to be able to relate to him man to man, not going to validate Bill's manhood by accepting him realistically as he is.

Bill and I talked for some time about his disappointment and anger at his father. Then a couple of months later they had another conversation. Bill's father made some empty statement about how other kids were deeply involved with drugs but not Bill. Bill could stand it no longer. He burst forth with a chronicle of his struggle not to become addicted to cocaine and heroin, his heavy daily use of marijuana and hashish, his struggle with the part of himself that wants to blot out pain with drugs, like his mother did with downs. His father got upset about this, but could say no more than, "You know I'm on your side!" He couldn't face the despair and loneliness and deprivation of love that drive Bill to comfort himself with drugs. He couldn't face the same feelings in his wife. And he can't face those feelings in himself, probably very similar, which drive him toward alcoholism himself.

What Bill must face now is that he has measured himself against his father and found that with all his problems he is closer to understanding what makes a man able to live and work happily than his father is. His father is successful in his work, he makes money, but he doesn't know how to enjoy his life or to get close to anyone. Bill now has to learn all those things his father could never teach him, and learn them through therapy, through a paid friend, a substitute father. Compared to other young men who also had no father when they were children, Bill is lucky, though. He can use therapy and his relationships with teachers at the School to validate himself as a man, to get the vital feedback he never got at home. How do my teachers and my therapist feel about what I do? And before he can care about how they feel about him, he must come to trust them and trust that their concern for him is real. A boy who had no father at home finds it very hard to develop love and trust for a father-person. Having been deprived of such love and trust when he needed it most, Bill must fight off the feeling that these people don't want to help him, except to say, "You know I'm on your side!"

Adolescents must learn to deal with their families. In the case of younger adolescents living at home, they must learn how to cope with the effect of their parents' feelings and behavior every single day. This can be terribly destructive. Amelia, at fourteen, has had to deal with serious parent problems while trying to go to school and manage her own life. She came to the School after overdosing with sleeping pills. When she got tense she would take a razor blade and slit her arms, sometimes just through the skin, sometimes a little deeper. I started talking to her and quickly found out that her parents were having a mortal struggle over their marriage, battling at home every day. I started to hold sessions with Amelia and her parents and found out that her father, another successful businessman, had not been in love with his wife almost from the beginning, but that he felt, "I just can't hurt anybody. So I won't leave her, even though I don't love her." He has a mistress and has had for years. When his wife found out about it last year, they began having battles almost every day, yelling and hitting each other. All five children hear each daily installment of this struggle. Amelia's mother has a psychiatrist who has advised her to confront her husband, "Give up the other woman or get out of this marriage!"—or so she has told Amelia. But she can't get up the courage to say these words, because he might really leave, and she doesn't feel strong enough to make it on her own. Her husband, on the other hand, doesn't feel he can simply leave the family, because he would then be responsible for hurting his wife, who says she still loves him. And so they battle on, and every day the kids must hear the fights and feel the displaced rage and frustration that these poor suffering parents vent on everyone in the house.

Amelia has found in the School a haven where she feels she belongs and where she can vent her own feelings as much as she needs to. Through her therapy in the group and with me individually, she has been able to follow a policy I suggested to her:

"Don't let your parents' battles and problems make you feel that you must wreck your own life. Your suicidal attempts don't achieve what you want, anyway. They don't make your parents come to their senses and start loving you again. You must take responsibility for yourself and your own life. You decide what is right for you to do, and do it."

Amelia has been able to do just that. She has stopped her dramatic demonstrations of despair and self-destructiveness, found a boyfriend, and has been doing adequate work in school. What has made that possible? Most likely, therapy and the School have provided a substitute family for her, parent-people who really care about her and who can show her ways to deal even with the desperate situation at home.

Older adolescents, long away from home, also need to deal with their families both in reality and in their own feelings. Bill's encounters with his father, and mine with my own father, are part of a process which needs to occur. In the cases where the parents and kids live together and we can have family therapy sessions, we can create new honesty in a family and everyone sees everyone else more honestly, more as people. But in a majority of instances we can't do that; the families are not around, or more commonly, parents are not interested in therapy that involve themselves. So coming to terms with your parents must now be done inwardly, evaluating your mother and father as human beings after you can understand what they have done for you and to you, and sometimes forgiving them their sins as parents. This is a vital part of becoming an adult; the mantle of understanding and judgment must pass to each of us as we grow up. The moment comes when we can no longer dismiss parents' behavior as a mystery of "grown-up" behavior, because we are not grown up ourselves. My decision to find my father by going to work with him, by learning his language, paid off later. I could understand him better; I came to like him. Later, when he remarried after my mother died, he came to me and we talked about his plan to marry again, talked as two men. That made me feel closer to him. And finally when he died I wanted to be with him, and I was. At the moment he finished his life I felt we had met and approved of each other as two adults, and that was tremendously important to me.

With my mother it was different. She taught us that you couldn't talk truthfully to her. She couldn't hear any messages that contradicted her goals for you. If you did what she wanted you to do, she liked you and she felt well. If you rebelled, she didn't admit anger or disappointment, she just got sick and went to bed depressed. So we could never face each other honestly as two adults, each with qualities that pleased the other and also with qualities that displeased the other. My feeling when she died was completely different: there was no resolution, no relief. She didn't know how I felt about her, so I could not see how she felt about my feelings toward her. The only thing I could do was to face my own feelings about my mother inwardly, in my own therapy. And it was hard and long.

Most of the kids at the School know that their parents do not approve of what they are becoming as people. Their values and their life styles are so different, the way they look at life is so opposed. So these kids feel inwardly doubtful of the validity of their position, even while overtly resisting their parents' attempts to change them.

When this gulf can be bridged, as when a father or mother finally see an adolescent's real life on his own territory, when for the first time one of them takes him seriously as a person and says, "I respect you," the relief and pleasure on both sides is enormous. When this can't happen, our School functions as an extended family, which can do exactly this: take each student's life style seriously and make honest comment on it. Then he can see where he is.

# 15 › Drugs and Creative Kids

THE OTHER DAY a twenty-year-old boy came to see me for some advice. Sam is tall, good-looking, friendly. He is the oldest son of two physicians. He told me the story of his life over the past year:

"I always figured I would go to college some place. But I didn't find anything in high school I wanted very much to do. I thought 'Why run off into college and just hack through it like I did in high school?' So I told my parents I wanted to take some time off and travel around, get a job if I ran out of money. I guess they were concerned about how vague my idea was, but what could they do about it? Anyway, they could see there was no use going to college if you don't know what for. They are really very understanding people. So I took my hundred bucks and started hitching across the country.

"I ran into some really good people, and of course some screwed-up characters. You know, queers who give you a ride and want to make it with you. Or salesmen who tell you to go home and get a straight job. I visited some of my friends who are on the west coast. All of them had changed a lot since they left Concord High School. A couple of them were really into the drug life. I mean, we had smoked pot together in Concord when we could get it, but they were now dealing in acid and speed and whatever they could get.

"The longer I spent with them, the more I got fascinated

*Drugs and Creative Kids*

with their kind of life. It was reall interesting, you know. Every day was a new challenge. I mean, would you get some stuff, would you sell it, would you get busted, would you get your money—it was all like a test of skill and cleverness. I got myself an apartment in a building out there. It was a wild place. A real classy modern apartment building with about twelve apartments. And everybody in the place was doing drugs. The place had been busted about fifteen times in the past year and a half. And we all knew the cops were watching the place constantly. So you see the game was a real challenge, how to make it under those conditions.

"Well, we all got together and put a couple of really good locks on the door and new keys. Then we wouldn't let anybody in that we didn't know really well. We would make all our contacts outside the place and we had really clever stashes for our stuff. It was a fun game to play. Us versus society, or at least the straight world of judges and cops. I got too involved with speed there, though. A friend showed me how to shoot speed, and it made me feel wonderful. You know, powerful and happy. And your mind works so fast! Even the crashes were not as bad as I thought they would be. Not the first ones, anyway."

"After about three months I began to see what I was doing and why. I knew speed was bad for me and that I would soon have to give it up or end in some hospital. What kept me doing it was not the need for the drug, because when I decided to quit I was able to quit and not go back to speed. But what fascinated me about the drug life was it was *real* to me. Your life must be real. Or it bores you to death. When I was living at home, life was comfortable but not *real*. My parents are good doctors, they care about their patients, and they are devoted to their work. Their work is *real* to them. When they get home they're tired, but pretty happy. There are no big problems in my home that I ever noticed. But at home and in high school I wasn't turned on. Life was boring to me.

"High school didn't get me excited about anything. I had

only two really exciting teachers, but the school didn't turn them on either. Both of them quit and went elsewhere to teach. But what can a student do about it? You can't all go elsewhere to school. A few of my friends went to private schools and most of them didn't get turned on there either. My high school is supposed to be one of the better ones, but I feel sorry for anybody who goes there. It's so *boring* you get so you break rules just to make something happen—for variety and excitement. I don't think life feels real to most of the teachers there, either, but older people seem to just accept that and don't make waves."

James, a sixteen-year-old boy who dropped out of high school and became addicted to heroin, told me:

"I was fifteen. I lived in Greenwich Village all that summer, sleeping on the roof of a tenement. One morning I woke up on the roof. I remember it was a really hot day. I picked my face up off the tar and I started staring at the chimney in front of me. And for once instead of thinking about how I could cop some dope today, I found myself knowing why I was doing it. And then the answer was so simple and obvious. Because it felt real. I mean the dope life involves you. It takes all your brains and guts just to live through a day in that life. But at least you're not asleep."

Marlene is a twenty-year-old girl who has recently been released from a women's prison after years of addiction to heroin. Marlene had become a prostitute to pay for her drugs:

"The drug scene was very intense to me. I mean you knew you were living. The pain was very strong in your body, where you could feel it. And the pleasure was clear and strong too. Now that I'm married and I have a better life, sometimes I still yearn for a life where there's even stronger involvement than marriage. At times I think the drug life was the most involving life I ever knew. I was hurt, angry, scared, but never bored."

A kid does not have to be disturbed to want a life of involvement and excitement. As I said before in this book, more and

*Drugs and Creative Kids*

more healthy young people rebel against the boring and constricting life imposed on them, by middle-class parents and conventional high schools, colleges, and jobs. And not only adolescents feel this constriction and strangulation of the self. A thirty-six-year-old man told me in all seriousness, "I am a better computer programmer since I smoke pot every day."

It is not that there is anything intrinsically wrong with the life style outlined for their children by most middle-class parents. The sequence:

High school—college—responsible job—marriage—raise a family is a fine sequence, offering many kinds of satisfaction to the younger generation. But the secret of satisfaction is not to be found in what you do, but in whether you *yourself* chose to do it. Here I must return to the idea I brought up earlier that every individual and his environment form a life system. Environment and individual interact in such complex ways that no outsider can hope to understand the totality of another's life. To those who respect the life systems of others, the greatest crime you can commit is to try in any way to *force* another being to change his life style. Of all who see this truth, those who appreciate it most profoundly are the so-called alienated youth, who label this comtemptuously as "mind-fucking." When they feel that a parent or teacher or policeman or psychiatrist is trying to pressure them or con them or force them into living in some style more harmonious with the values of the nation at large or to make them obey some law they do not see the sense of, they will resist coercion. Overtly or secretly they resist being molded. As the Harvard strike poster shouts, "Strike . . . because they are squeezing the life out of you!"

Many of our most intelligent and creative young people are being driven to find a sense of realness in the drug life and by dropping out of school and running away from home. Because they become alienated from school and home, many of our best adolescents have lost contact with what is valuable about our society and with the finest personal qualities of those adults who sincerely wish to guide them. And not only do kids who cut themselves off from "straight society" lose the chance to learn what the best parents and teachers have to offer, but there are real dangers in the dropping-out process itself, especially when a lot of drugs are involved.

#### MARIJUANA

I am not impressed with the "dangers" of marijuana. The trouble with marijuana is almost entirely legal trouble, and most of the problem will vanish when and if it is legalized. This does not mean that I don't know anyone who has had difficulties with marijuana and its cousin hashish. When kids smoke grass every day, or in large amounts, a kind of lethargy comes over them and they don't feel like doing school work or anything else physically or mentally active. And the amount of actual creative *work* done by artists who smoke a lot of dope is much less than when they are straight.

But most young people quickly learn that in reasonable amounts on a weekend or at a party, or in some pleasant place with a friend or two, marijuana and hashish give you a pleasant high without after effects. And they seem to regard these experiences as worth the legal hassles resulting if you get arrested.

There is no doubt that kids with deep personal and family problems can get a pot "habit"—but only in the sense that they use pot as a way of hiding from life and avoiding the challenges they fear they can't meet. And that is a problem. I have noticed that pot seems to be used more by kids who live in homes where there is poor communication with parents and who go to schools where they are not stimulated or challenged by good teaching. In my opinion it is mostly the boredom of middle-class homes and schools that leads kids to search for more ways to get high. I recommend that anyone looking for more facts about marijuana consult the book

*Drugs and Youth* by Coles, Brenner and Meagher. My main point here is not to defend marijuana, but to stress that the use of large amounts of pot is related to the boredom and emptiness of middle-class life for adolescents. Adults facing the same boredom and emptiness tend to use other drugs. Many of the parents of my young patients have serious alcohol and tranquilizer problems.

**LSD AND PSYCHEDELICS**

On the other hand, I have already seen enough disturbances relating from the use of LSD and other real psychedelics that I do *not* regard them as harmless, even the "gentle" mescaline. Two principal dangers stem from the use of LSD, peyote, psilocybin, mescaline, and their relatives (this does not include marijuana):

1. "Bad trips": When an inner emotional disturbance exists, like great repressed anger, fear, or guilt, a psychedelic drug experience can magnify this feeling and panic the tripper. Even when one's inner feelings are in good order, a disturbance in the environment during a psychedelic trip can cause a panic or paranoid reaction, for instance, if the police arrive or mother comes home unexpectedly or if a car nearly hits you or if a stranger at a party turns out to be hostile to you and attacks you while you are tripping. Though trippers like to believe that if you are consciously feeling well and you trip in pleasant surroundings with trusted friends, you will always be alright, there are some bad trips that occur despite all preparations. Despite this, tripping on LSD, mescaline, and peyote has helped many people get a glimpse of the self in relationship to the environment, to see one's life system in busy operation from a new perspective. Still, tripping to me remains "Russian roulette." Some people will get hurt, and not always the people a psychiatrist would label as emotionally fragile. I myself have taken one trip on LSD and several on mescaline in

addition to caring for patients who have had bad trips, so I speak from personal experience, even though my own few trips were of great value to me and not bad trips.

2. Prolonged reactions: There definitely are long-term psychotic reactions to the psychedelic drugs. A disturbance in knowing who you are, where you are, or what is going on may occur after the best of trips and last for months, even putting you in the hospital. This is true even if you have tripped only after months of holding off, and it can happen even on your first trip.

**SPEED AND HEROIN**

I put these in the same category because, though speed is considered an "up" and heroin a "down," they both will give you a drug habit. Users quickly need more of them to get the desired reaction, and the depressions when crashing off "speed" can be devastating, just as bad as the withdrawal symptoms in body and mind when coming off heroin. People have committed suicide while crashing after a long bout on speed.

Another danger connected with dropping out by the drug route is getting arrested, convicted, and maybe committed to a training school or jail. Yet sometimes when a child gets "busted" for drugs, this wakes his parents up to his alienation, and under the shock of the crisis some real communication takes place between parents and child. I have seen this lead to new and better family relationships. But more often, the whole process of paying up to a thousand dollars for a lawyer and facing the judge and the neighbors causes parents a great deal of anger and humiliation and deepens the gulf that may already exist between parents and child. Fathers denounce and "wash their hands of" their sons, mothers weep, and guilt and rage flow freely on all sides. For some very angry adolescents, getting arrested now becomes a weapon with which to revenge themselves upon despised parents. *Drugs and Youth,* the book to which I already referred, is a good source of information about all drugs used by youth today and their legal and other consequences.

If more police officers were better trained to understand the human problems of adolescents, if more juvenile court judges could understand the underlying struggle for a life with meaning, a life that feels *real*, if more probation officers knew how to open up honest communication with adolescent probationers, if only there were half enough probation officers so that they had time even to talk with the adolescents under their charge—but these are ifs at present, and even the very best juvenile probation officers agree that probation cannot make up for an empty life.

Commitment to "correctional" or training schools is generally harmful to intelligent and creative young people. We have in this country very few such schools that can meet the needs of confused adolescents. The average training school anywhere in the nation is a repressive custodial institution where conformity and submission are demanded; very few inmates (or "wards," as the euphemism goes) can find there a close or honest relationship with anyone they can admire. If these adolescents felt bored, constricted, unexcited by life at home, all these feelings are generally very much worsened in the average youth "correctional" institution.

The most insidious danger of the dropping-out sequence is the least obvious. It is the dreary fact that most kids who drop out of school, home, and the "straight life" are not able to find in the "hip life" the sense of exhilaration and self-expression they were looking for. Alone or with their dropout peers, they still feel empty, going no place. And now, having broken contact with the rest of society, they find it almost impossible to create a life with meaning. Here and there, perhaps in a commune out in the woods, such a life evolves. Certainly most communal living attempts I have heard about have been noble failures, partly because of lack of money or lack of skills needed for self-preservation, but primarily because of the insufficient emotional maturity of the participants. When you live together, you must accept the feelings people have about each other—love, hate, jealousy, competitiveness, the whole range of human emotions. When we designed our own school community, we realized that people were going to feel all these emotions, and we set up our weekly group therapy sessions to explore and deal with them as they arose. These sessions helped a lot of people grow up in the sense that they learned to deal openly with the problems of a group enterprise and thus to become a close-knit and loving community.

Psychiatrists who evaluate families have tended to think of "sick" and "healthy" families. I think it is much more relevant to think of families who are open about feelings and families who are not. A family or school or any social structure where feelings cannot come out freely and be resolved is an unhealthy one to grow up in. When a parent is neurotic or psychotic, this prevents him from dealing openly with his own feelings and those of others because he is guilty or afraid of what he feels inside. That prevents communication and drives the adolescent out to find more intense real-feeling experiences somewhere else. *Realness* can be found at home if parents will set the example of sharing feelings openly with their kids. And if *realness* exists at home, there is less need to find it in drugs or dropping out.

In our School we have created an atmosphere of *realness*. Feelings are dealt with openly by staff and students alike. We don't judge or compare. In this atmosphere drug use by our students has generally decreased greatly. This has made me feel even more certain that a main reason for the use of drugs was to find a sense of realness and intensity of experience. We have seen an *inverse* relationship between creative work-play and use of drugs. As creative channels open up before the creative adolescent, he needs less drug highs. This is particularly true for highly creative people, who must constantly find original ways to express themselves or become desperate.

This particular motivation, the search for channels of expression, is characteristic of the highly creative child. But it is unknown to most parents and schools. Highly creative kids not only enjoy creative learning opportunities, they need them. When deprived of these channels the resultant desperation goes to the core of the personality.

For other kids less urgently creative, the feature of our School which has turned them away from drug-centered lives is more the intimacy and realness of the group communication. Starting in group meetings and classes, then finding friends at the School, visiting them, going places together, many lonely kids find a new life. But this is a life that is part of a community, where problems are discussed, where relationships just don't mysteriously end, leaving you wondering why the other person never called you any more. Adolescent life is full of such endings, the inevitable painful ruminations. "Why doesn't anyone like me? What's wrong with me?" Many lonely, cut off kids without social skills turn to drugs. At the School it works differently. Sally can ask in the group:

"Why doesn't anyone get close to me? I go around looking for someone to care, and no one pays any attention to me!"

When Sally asked that, several members of the group replied:

**Hugo**: "When you were near me working on a batik, I tried to talk to you three times and you didn't say more than a word to me. I felt you didn't want to be close to me."

**Michelle**: "Yes, that happened to me too. I got the impression you didn't like me."

That night Sally found out she was so afraid she would be rejected that she was stiff with tension whenever she tried to talk to someone. She also remembered that her mother was so frightened of human contact that she had to write down what she wanted to tell people, lest in her panic she forget entirely what she wanted to say.

Finally, Sally realized that she feels so empty inside, so devoid of value, that no one could possibly care about her. So she is angry in advance at the inevitable rejection, feeling empty and unloved. Sally has gotten in touch with these feelings. Now what? I suggested that when anyone in the group wanted to get close to Sally or they felt her locking them out they should go up to her and tell her immediately what they were feeling. I would too. We will see how this works. It has helped others.

So through the opening of creative channels and opening the paths to intimacy we have relieved many of the pressures that lead many of the young to drug use. And they use less drugs.

# PART 4 ›
# Conclusion: "I Am What I Am, But Not Yet"

# 16 › So Far

IN A CONVENTIONAL SCHOOL there are obvious ways to report the "progress" of a student. He got an A in math, a B in English, he graduated or he dropped out, he went on to Harvard or he now works in a lumberyard. Such a school sets itself the goal of teaching certain subjects and it sets up ways to measure how much the students have absorbed. Since most suburban American high schools exist for two main purposes:

1. to keep the kids busy and "out of trouble"
2. to get them into college

these goals are measurable. In my part of the country, some communities dismiss high school administrators if the percentage of graduates entering grade A colleges drops a bit, just as a baseball team fires a manager when the "games won" total drops and the gate receipts dip.

But when the goal of a school is to help the young students reach fuller humanity and to help each meet life in his own unique way, how can we measure success? Should an art school report each year how many paintings and sculptures were sold by the graduates, and how much money they got for them? Neill, founder of the famous Summerhill school in England, reported that his goal was to help the children grow up to be better people, so that any follow-up study should attempt somehow to evaluate how the old grads are functioning in *human* terms as well as by job description and income levels.

As I ponder how to describe the results of our two years of working together in the School We Have, I am faced with hard questions. What is progress? How could we have done better? What did each of our students need and did we help him find it?

I am reminded of an experiment performed by some pediatricians years ago. Infants were exposed to an array of different foods, all within their reach, and allowed to eat whichever they chose. The results were interesting: though each infant might choose to eat entirely sweets or starches at any one time, over the long run they provided a balanced diet for themselves and they grew and developed better than many infants do on diets set up for them by adults.

In the same way, our School provides an array of possible subjects and teacher relationships from which each prospective member may select what he wants to do and with whom he wants to work. At this moment any student can study drama, moviemaking, photography, yoga, meditation, painting, sculpture (including welding metal), folksinging and guitar, jazz and rock and blues instruments, aikido, batik, sewing, cooking, leathercraft, and silversmithing. We offer individual instruction in woodwind and reed instruments and music theory. Among our teachers, young people can select those with whom they would like to work. Anyone is free to take all the classes or only one. You can change classes or add classes any time you wish. It is interesting that there is not much skipping around from class to class. Like the infants in the diet experiment, our young people select what they wish and it often seems to be what they need. As I mentioned while describing the way the School works (see Chapter 3), trusting the students pays off.

Take the case of Don, a young man I have mentioned already a couple of times. When he came to us at twenty-two (see Chapter 11), Don had gotten little benefit from at least five years of therapy with several different therapists. His angry, pessimistic, almost paranoid feelings against his parents and society had been deepened by a hospitalization and a course of shock treatment at the hands of a prominent psychoanalyst. When I treated Don, it was before our School had started, and in almost two years of attempted "insight therapy" he had learned nothing new about himself.

*Father's position:* "This boy has done nothing with himself all his life. He dreams, he evades responsibility. He has disappointed my hopes for him. I don't know if he'll ever make anything of himself, much less a doctor or any sort of professional. He just somehow lacks some vital ingredient—he always has. I'm tired of supporting him and helping him with ridiculous activities like jazz."

*Mother's position:* "I feel sorry for Don, because he and his father are so far from understanding one another. But my husband is right—Don's life is a mess. I can understand his love for music—I love it too. But he should study classical music from a recognized teacher and practice at least an hour a day. How can we get him to see that he's on a path that leads nowhere?"

*Don's position:* "My father is down on me. He's been against me as long as I can remember because I don't want to follow in his footsteps as a surgeon or some other professional career. He won't help me with what I want to do, only with what he wants me to do. My mother is less tough than he is, but in a softer way she is trying to get me into *their* kind of life too. I don't want to be a pillar of the community, a prominent doctor, or a symphony musician! I guess everybody—well, nearly everybody—is like my parents: they only use you to get what they want from you. You can't really trust people. If you do, they'll screw you one way or another."

When our School started, Don himself selected his blues

piano teacher. I recounted earlier how Don believed that Dave was the man he felt could teach him to play the blues, and he brought Dave to me. Don spent four-hour lessons with Dave. They developed an intense relationship. Though Don often felt jealous and angry at Dave, he respected his talent and learned a lot of piano from him. Don also got interested in astrology. As I reported in an earlier chapter, the astrology teacher became interested in him too, and showed how he could understand his life of depression and disappointment in astrological terms. All during his year of involvement with astrology and blues, Don was in individual psychotherapy with me. He was uninterested in my ideas about why he felt as he did. He needed concrete help, he felt. Like a much younger child, he was at first completely dependent. He could often be found around the place, sleeping in someone's bed, taking a shower, eating something he found in the kitchen. More than once he took bottles of wine from my closet. He drank a lot, and once, after I told him he could not move into my home to live, he got drunk and was found lying unconscious in the snow.

But Don began to find something he needed in our program. He began to become more independent. He got some music jobs and he made a successful relationship with a girl for the first time in his life. Now he lives with this girl. He is more autonomous than he has ever been, and there's much less of the angry dependent feeling about him. He drinks less, too.

In discussing Don's story with a psychoanalyst friend of mine, his comment was, "This is a transference cure." What analysts mean by this term is that someone got better because of a strengthening relationship with a therapist or someone who acts as an ideal parent-figure for him. If this relationship ends, the patient falls back into his old patterns of unsuccessful adaptation to life, gets sick again. In the psychoanalytic system, only the "insight cure" frees the patient from his conflicts. He must see what is wrong with him and renounce his illness through full awareness of it.

If it is true that Don's improvement is temporary and due to his relationship with Dave or the astrology teacher or myself, I can't understand why he continues to do so well. He has not had a piano lesson in months, his astrology teacher has moved away, and he has not visited me in six months. In one sense and one sense only, though, I think my analyst friend is right: Don started out expressing his childish rage and dependency towards us, and we for a while were parents to him, better parents, for we took it, and continued to accept him. But then Don started to develop towards autonomy, as a kind of musical apprentice to Dave. His relationship with me became limited to discussion of practical problems ("ego material," as the jargon goes); the dependent demands are gone. Whatever we may call it, Don has rounded a vital corner of his life. He can play music and now he can love also. He is doing better than ever, and for the past several months he has needed no therapy at all.

Betsy (see Chapter 5) stayed with us for several months. She wrote poetry and made a close relationship with her writing teacher. When in her therapy with me she reached the vital point of admitting her great need for a mother to care for her and love her like a baby, she got into an angry battle with her mother, who had never been able to give her this kind of love. Betsy took off immediately for California and got a job in Los Angeles. I heard almost nothing from her for almost six months, and then she came back and resumed therapy at her own expense. Later she went to another city to live with a man she loves. Unlike Don, Betsy found at our School both a strengthening apprenticeship (with her writing teacher) and insight as well through her therapy with me.

Both Don and Betsy are now more complete people. They are no longer so much troubled kids as young adults. They are now trying to live without demanding that some parent-figure give them this or that, and they are no longer blaming their difficulties on someone else.

James is a boy who became a heroin addict at fifteen. Earlier, I told the story of how he realized why he was living an addict's life. James came to our art and drama classes, creative writing, and group therapy for five months. He was never in individual therapy. After this brief involvement, he felt ready to move on and to do real things in the real world. He has a steady job as a metalworker, but his main interest is in helping people. He set up art classes for black children in the ghetto and later worked on providing a place where runaway adolescents can come for help. He feels the existing agencies do not do enough for the most disturbed young people, and he wants to correct this situation. He has no more involvement with drugs; he prefers meditation.

Dom (Chapter 5) has "graduated" after two years at the School. The first effect our School had on Dom was to get him excited about learning how to do things. Sculpture, then acting, then making movies, then electric guitar. The second effect was to make Dom decide to enter individual therapy with me. And just as he started to see me, one of our group therapy sessions had a third effect on him.

Dom had just voiced one of his ringing opinions about something, in a voice loaded with anger. Someone pointed out he sounded angry. He denied it flatly, adding that no matter whatever happened to him, he never got angry, never. The group broke up with laughter at this one. Then followed an hour of dodging and twisting, with Dom trying desperately to convince us he never gets angry. But with all the authorities and the kids as well patiently showing him how he was showing anger, Dom finally saw it.

After this point, Dom began to face his jealousy of his father and his anger at him. When he took that step, he began to understand his fear of hurting anybody and his great fear of competition. He has become more and more reliable and he has invested real energy into his creative activities. Dom is now clearly going to make it. He has a full-time job, lives on his own.

Sometimes I recall how once a clinic psychiatrist got Dom to tell the members of a staff conference how he made a collage; this was at the clinic Dom attended before he came to the School.

*Psychiatrist*: "How do you go about making one of your collages?"
*Dom*: "Well, I cut out magazine pictures and whatever else looks good to me, and I paste them together."
*P.*: "How do you decide on the composition?"
*Dom*: "I just put in whatever seems to go right in the place I'm working on. It sort of composes itself."

After Dom left the conference room, the clinic psychiatrist pointed out to us how this was an example of Dom's "disorganized and structureless way of life" and an example of "how disturbed he was." Like most mental health professionals, the psychiatrist had no special ability to evaluate creative works on their own merits. So I must add still another effect of Dom's leaving the psychiatric clinic and coming into our program: Dom was now at last in an environment where people *know* that there is no right way to do art or music or acting or anything. There is your *own* way. How do we know that? Because every one of our staff has had to find it out for himself in his own creative field. By this, I do not mean there are no techniques to learn and no discipline to master. I mean that each person must decide *for himself* which techniques and methods are relevant to the goal he has decided to attain. He then learns out of motivation, not out of authority externally applied. When you get down to the essence of any subject of study, I believe the same applies. Good education works from the child's own wishes and his natural style; only *bad* education enforces a style upon the student. Way back at the beginning, when Dick (our first art teacher) was looking for a description of the way he was going to teach he wrote: "I will take each student further out along *his own trip,* until we reach the edge of space!"

What has happened to Brad? (Chapter 5) Very early in the development of our program, Brad found it harder and harder to cope with the group, particularly the psychotherapy sessions. In one session he held the floor for a long time, telling us how he goes into the black ghettos dressed in his hippy clothes and how often he has been beaten and threatened. The reaction of the other kids was: "Why do such a stupid thing? You don't prove anything by it. It's a self-destructive act. You'd be better off putting your energy into your painting, or getting a job to get some money."

Unlike Jack, Brad was unable to use the group's help to re-examine his own behavior. He became more bitter and mistrustful of people. He closed up and stopped attending the group. I continued to see him alone, but for months he told me little about his feelings and plunged into repeated bouts with psychedelic drugs and dangerous risk-running. At one point he got hold of a gun. I had to threaten to put him into the hospital several times. And by the time I started writing this final chapter, I felt I had to report failure with Brad. He had missed three appointments with me.

Then I got in touch with him and he came to see me again. He now has an apartment where he lives with his new girlfriend. He has stayed off drugs almost entirely for the past six months, and he has a job. A couple of days after our appointment, Brad called me to ask how he could help a girl he knows who has become paranoid. He was able to agree that if she did not go with him to see a psychiatrist, her parents would have to be told that she is in bad shape, and they might need to get her into a hospital. Even though he hates hospitals and has been committed himself, Brad could see this might be necessary. Brad's judgment has improved and his life is stabilized. To what extent his involvement with our group or his relationship with me have helped him achieve this I don't know.

Chester (Chapter 5) never came to our group therapy and quit taking writing classes after a few weeks. He visited me alone off and on, mostly off. He did not go back to college. For a while he worked steadily as a cabinetmaker's helper. Then he did a lot of traveling across the country by himself. He tried to work alone to control his problem with drinking. Once in a while he came in for advice when he had a decision to make. Our relations were friendly, but Chester made it clear for over a year that he would not depend upon anyone, nor accept anyone's authority. Then he made a decision—he needed help—and he returned to me and to the School to find it. He faced some of the underlying feelings that have led to his drinking and his depression. For the first time I felt Chester is seriously in therapy. He then returned to college in a new school, designing his own program.

Patty (Chapter 5) finished high school and worked part-time during her senior year. She began to be able to handle her relations with boys and drugs so that she stayed out of trouble. She came to drama class, where she became one of the most reliable members. She lost a lot of weight and looks really attractive. The angry self-destructive tone has gone from her voice and her behavior. She is still dramatic, but she now wins people's attention more with her alertness and humor than with crises. Patty "graduated" from our School and went on as a theater student in college.

Chris (Chapter 5) quit coming to our group therapy and classes after only a few visits. He became a rebel from our place, much as he had from other establishments. He continued to see me for a few months, but missed about half his appointments. He moved into a house of his own far out in the country, all alone, but as yet I haven't heard whether he started the commune he frequently talked about. I don't think he got much out of his therapy with me, although he stayed

*So Far*

out of any further legal troubles and got off probation. He dropped in recently asking about life in zen monasteries. On this visit he showed for the first time that he now feels responsibility to get his own head straightened out.

Vic (Chapter 5) never liked group activities, but came to see me for therapy for about six months. He has not gotten into new tangles with the law, but still faces old drug charges that date back to before I knew him. Recently he went through a spell of depression while awaiting trial. I have been able to show him that he relates to society in the same angry rebellious way he did to his father, but he does not find this kind of "insight" relevant to his situation. He prefers to seek peace of mind through spiritual channels. For example, he had over two thousand dollars stolen recently by a friend, but Vic took the attitude that this was just as well, because the whole "money trip" was probably the cause of his troubles anyway. The theft he saw as a lesson—like the Buddha, he must give up caring about profit and live more simply. He was not angry or depressed when he told me this, but looked genuinely comfortable and relieved.

I believe the grasping for money represented a substitute for the love and closeness Vic never found at home. So money for him is something he yearned for but could never hold on to. Thus, no matter how big the deal, Vic would always lose it or be punished and suffer somehow. Vic is trying to renounce money, the symbol of the problem, yet can't see the problem itself. So my predictions for him are guarded at this point.

What about Wanda? (Chapter 5) She made several good friends at our School, but she has held onto the position of critic and rebel. Wanda still feels militant about her blackness and about her womanhood. I don't feel we have gotten close enough to her, or perhaps I should say I don't feel Wanda has let us get close enough to her to show her it is really safe to trust people, particularly white people. But we are still trying.

Who has been helped? As I think about the two hundred young people who have been involved with our School for even a little while, I am convinced that I was wise at the start not to let psychiatric "diagnosis" play any part in preventing anyone from joining us. Some of those who were officially the sickest have benefited most from our program. The idea, "We can work together if the child can relate to someone here," still holds, and it is the key to getting into our program. A very few of our young people have stayed with us at the edge of our little community, perhaps talking only to one teacher, rarely coming to group therapy sessions. Most have been at the center soon after joining the School.

We have also been wise, I believe, to be extremely flexible and easy as to how involved anyone needs to become, and as to what is expected. For example, Rachel had been attending our group therapy for almost a year without ever saying anything that revealed her feelings. And no one put much pressure on her to share them. Then suddenly one evening she poured out some of her deepest feelings, her agonizing doubts over whether anyone cares for her, her great desire to be loved, and her fear of reaching for love lest she be rebuffed and her feelings of worthlessness confirmed. And when after all this time Rachel spoke out, it was to the group, not me alone. She just finally felt that she could trust us. And she came through. After that, people could get closer to her.

When I try to figure out if the School We Have has helped these kids, and if so, how it has helped, I come out with something hard to put into words. Dom has stabilized his way of life, quit his extravagant drug-taking, and is working hard on the guitar. He is supporting himself now. And Patty is in college studying theater, which is her own choice. She too is no longer involved in dangerous situations with sex and drugs. Vic has not been arrested for any new offense since he came to us. Brad, Chester, and Wanda have "graduated" from our School.

The consensus of the kids in our School is that after getting involved with us, they take less drugs than they did before and they don't get into trouble with the police. In fact only three students in our School have gone to court since joining us. A great many had been in trouble with the authorities before they came to us. So in concrete terms, we have seen our kids taking less drugs, staying out of court.

But much more important is the fact that the School has helped a large number of our kids commit themselves, not only to standard goals like full-time jobs or going to college as such, but to goals of their own choosing—music, dance, theater, painting, teaching, and helping people, so that when those who have dropped out return to school it is because they are motivated to learn about something they really care about. Staying out of court, taking less drugs, not getting pregnant are important enough, but they are *negative* goals. Committing yourself to learning how to do something you really care about is a *positive* goal, one that your parents may well have been unable to achieve.

And one other result of their involvement in our school is that a great many of our kids have become able to reveal their honest feelings to each other, and thus have become able to make more intimate and satisfying relationships—to offer love and to find love. That is where the group therapy aspect of the School has done the most.

The School We Have (a student embroidered us a handmade school banner with that title on it) has encouraged the growth of intimacy also because it is the right size. It is small enough so that everybody can know everybody else, but big enough so the shy, the frightened, and the somewhat paranoid can inhabit the safe corners while keeping in touch with what is going on, until, like Rachel, they take the plunge and reveal how they feel. And they retain the right *never* to reveal themselves. The kids can be trusted to get more involved when they are ready. I have been a member of small therapy groups, and I did not like the atmosphere of "enforced tell-all." In a tiny group if you don't choose to reveal yourself, you may be the *only* silent one, and others may put extreme pressure on you to reveal yourself, to do as they did. In our group, we work from motivation, not pressure. I am sure there are some who will wait longer than Rachel did, but when they say what they want to say, it will have been worth waiting for.

# 17 › Dynamics

INTERESTED IN HOW adults teach values to kids in societies less complicated and alienated than our own, my wife and I visited a village of the Giriama tribe near the Indian Ocean coast of Kenya. Realizing that visitors are interested in their music and dances, these villagers have learned that they can perform their corn-grinding dance, circumcision dance, and other ceremonies for visitors to make some money. To see these performances at their proper time and full-length one would have to stay in the area a long time. Aware that we were watching an early stage in the commercialization of these traditional rituals, we attended what turned out to be a performance involving almost everyone in the village. When we arrived, children were sent off by the headman to round up the men who would drum for the dance, the girls who would dance and sing, and others who would bring and take care of the props (corn-grinding mortars, baskets, etc.). While the drumheads were being heated over a fire, children and adults put on costumes in huts around a central dance arena, a flat place in the center of the village. Discipline was remarkable, without much obvious effort on the part of the headman. Soon some twenty girls from three to sixteen years old were lined up, wearing small skirts made of strips of rough cloth and bracelets. The headman also collected a few older performers in their late teens and twenties and began blowing on a buffalo horn to start the drummers drumming and the chorus chanting. Then he took over as a kind of combination artistic director and sergeant-at-arms. He sang the lead while the chorus responded, danced throughout, and circulated among the performers keeping them in line, getting them to sing louder, keeping things moving. A couple of times, dissatisfied with the performance of a lead dancer, he simply hauled her out by the arm, sent her off to the dressing hut, and led in a replacement from the chorus line. The show was lively and fascinating, the performances of high quality, and the pace was brisk as any Broadway musical or TV production.

But what was most important was the obvious fact that *everybody* in the village was involved in these rituals. From age three or four, when the girls become part of the chorus, to old age, when the elders become part of the audience, still repeating the chorus, the rituals unite every one in a shared awareness of what they are doing and why. As among the "pig people" in New Guinea, whose lives were described to me by my anthropologist friend, there is a deep sharing of goals and techniques in such village societies.

Aware that we in America have lost this unanimity of goals and life styles, our adolescent children seek some sense of unity with others. I was reminded suddenly of the Giriama dances when a twenty-one-year-old girl described to me her life in a Boston commune: "We all work, mostly in the community, and bring our salaries back to the common fund. A few of us stay home and clean and cook while the rest work in town. We do secretarial work, house cleaning, painting, carpentry, anything—the difference is that all our earnings are shared. We decide together how to spend our money. If someone is in trouble, like needing an operation or paying off a debt, we all help him. I feel less lonely than when I was on my own, looking for apartments, having trouble with roommates, finding jobs, trying to make some kind of life for myself and never finding it."

After this girl stopped writing to her parents they became

uneasy, wondering whether her deep devotion to this commune and its monastic austerity was healthy, or whether she might be in some sort of masochistic surrender to the will of the group because she had failed to make a success of her life as an autonomous individual. They came to see me to ask how they might find out whether she was alright. One thing the mother said stuck in my mind: "I don't understand Alice's subjection to this kind of dictatorship. When her father and I made rules, she evaded them and rebelled. And some of them were the same rules she now accepts totally. Clean your room, help with the dishes, get a job and save your money. Why does she do these things in the commune so willingly, while she refused to do them for her own parents?"

These are not unloving nor particularly disturbed parents. They are intelligent liberals, not unduly lax in disciplining their children, and they do care deeply about their daughter's life. When she told me she was worried that Alice might be depressed and suffering but unwilling to reveal it to anyone, the mother wept bitterly. How was I to tell her that the sacrament of Alice's commune is the *sharing* of decisions and goals. Alice feels she *belongs* there and she is willing to do whatever it takes to continue to belong to this group she has chosen. This makes me think of what we have evolved in the School We Have.

The School works because it has become an extended family, a tribe, or commune for the kids who have chosen to belong to it. Starting with kids who don't know what sort of lives they want or are capable of, the School shows them some more creative and honest life-style possibilities, exemplified by the teachers and students who have been there a long time already. The newcomers get to know these people really well. They get to know people who are living more authentic lives, and they begin to realize that a more authentic life is not only possible to create, but essential to strive for. Here there is an enormous difference from the Giriama tribal village as well as the Boston commune. We do not insist upon the sacrament of doing what *everybody* does, but rather the sacrament of finding what you yourself want to do, no matter how long it takes you to decide. But like the village and the commune, we share caring for each other. We come to know about each other not merely the intimate facts known to any family, but much more than any family knows about any of its members. Alice's parents have no idea of Alice's intrapsychic life. They are painfully out of touch with her view of herself, her search, her values since adolescence. At the School we show people how to reveal the deepest secrets of their lives, how to trust the group to understand and guide, *without* insisting upon any particular kind of behavior. Eccentricity and uniqueness are accepted wholeheartedly. We are there to help kids find out how *they* want to lead their lives, not how *we* want them to live. A great example is the young man who announced his "graduation" from our School by inviting us all to his baptism into a christian church.

**THE HEALTHY ADOLESCENT**

The adolescent whose personality is basically intact, who is without deep intrapsychic problems (about half our population), has one overriding problem: *What kind of life to choose?* (Identity crisis, in Erikson's terms; "normative adolescent turmoil" in conventional psychiatric terms.)

This group is made up of kids who come to the School out of interest in what we are teaching and how it is taught. Some of them are referred clinically, but turn out not to have deep psychoneurotic problems or other major intrapsychic disturbances. These kids have passed through the major stages of their psychic development prior to adolescence successfully. Their problem is mainly the one which faces each adolescent in our society: How to become your own person in your own way, and how to make the important people and institutions in your life recognize your individuality. Our School can be observed to affect these healthy adolescents in the following sequence of ways:

*Phase I*: In this beginning phase, the School provides the intact adolescent with a wide choice of authentic life-style examples. The new student becomes involved with teachers and peers at the School, and he begins to see in the group various stages of evolution toward maturity. The newest kids tend to express at first their resistance to life-style pressures imposed by parents, schools and so on: "I will *not* live the way my parents want me to." This has often been expressed in behavior which expresses the further position of alienation, "I will not only *not* live as they want me to, I will live as *differently* from my parents as I can!" This leads the unrealized adolescent to acts of overt rebellion against his parents' world via:

Delinquency
School failure or "underachievement"
Sexual rebellion—pregnancy, V.D., and complications
Drug experimentation

Although commonly rebellion through drugs is expressed through the use of the relatively harmless pot and hash, often psychedelic tripping begins this way. This can and occasionally does lead to psychotic and other prolonged reactions and may require mental hospitalization. In my experience, psychedelic tripping done as an angry rebellion against restricting parents and the adult world seems more often to result in paranoid trips (probably because of the angry and oppressed state of mind before and during the trip). These have depressing effects upon the personality. Recently, more and more intact adolescents are getting involved with more dangerous drugs, speed and the opiates. These, of course, have their own very serious complicating effects—addiction, jail, overdose, death. Fortunately the usual pattern of drug experimentation by intact adolescents is limited to marijuana, hashish, and some psychedelics. Some of these experiences can teach the adolescent a great deal about his mental and emotional richness and may become key experiences in his emotional life. But unfortunately with illegal tripping he has very little chance to discuss these experiences with understanding older people. If he happens to be in psychotherapy with an unusually open-minded therapist, his trip can be discussed and its insights turned into better living solutions.

*Phase II*: After some experiments in antiestablishment thinking and action, the adolescent who enters the School notices:

"There are others here like me. They like it here."

"They don't label you sick or delinquent here."

Simultaneously, he notices:

"The things I care about can be learned here"

These classes in fascinating subjects, taught by fascinating people, become the "bait" that attracts the new student to the School. Later, when he begins to become involved in group therapy with his peers and some teachers, he tends to express:

"The people here are amazingly open about their feelings."

He may also express:

"I could never be that free."

What he observes is that the important thing in the group is openness. He begins to want to be more open about his own feelings, to talk more freely about himself in group therapy. At first he may fear that if the group comes to know him deeply, it will reject him or disapprove of him. But as he watches others bring up their deepest fears and feelings, he sees that no one is rejected, no one is disapproved of, though the group may criticize some things its members may do. Soon, usually within a month, the new student takes the plunge. At the School this is like a rite of passage. You are not really a full member of the School somehow until you have let your group in on some of the most important feelings and facts of your life. The heavier (more difficult and painful) they are, the more respect you earn for having revealed them. This is a general "groupism"—in all the groups I've led or been a member of, this phenomenon occurs.

From here on, the basically intact adolescent, now a full member of his therapy group, has pretty smooth sailing. He can be trusted to bring up whatever hangups he has, when he feels ready to talk about them. The "journey towards the center of the self" that characterizes all psychotherapy takes place at a pace that suits the individual. This is a vital point; I have always felt that aggressively led groups, where leaders attack members and force them to deal with their deepest problems here and now, are assaults upon the ego that may be dangerous. Recent research tends to show that emotional casualties of such groups may reach 10 percent; one of every ten members suffering symptoms of stress well after the group sessions have ended, and some members may suffer very serious breakdowns under this treatment. At the School, the group leadership style is kind and loving overall, though it varies from leader to leader. We don't go in for aggressive high-pressure groups.

Anywhere from six months to two years after starting in the School, the intact adolescent finds a way to tell us he has gotten what he came for and he feels ready to "graduate." If he dropped out of high school or college, he may go back, but much more often on his own terms, not those of his parents or of the school authorities. He may enroll in a creative arts school or a conservatory or find a college or high school where he can select his own program of courses in an environment he likes. He is stronger and freer now after being at the School, and knows it is his own life, and he can insist on living it the way he chooses. He may go to work—sometimes in a job where he uses skills he learned with us, a craft or apprenticeship or some form of helping others. If he chooses a job purely to make money, he usually has a pretty good idea by now what he wants the money for, and this makes a meaningless "slave" job easier to bear and easier to quit when he has the money he needs for the moment. A good number of our "graduates" travel for awhile, wandering around this country or abroad. Most of this travel is not aimless drifting, not avoidance of life, but a genuine search for a self-selected life style integrated with nature, ecology, art, love, perhaps in a commune or kibbutz, perhaps in less concrete arrangements. As long as these voyages are conducted independently and responsibly, parents can feel assured that these adolescents will eventually find a life situation that suits them, though it may take a couple of years. A good many of our graduates find that they can't feel satisfied with a life-style choice that does not center about an art they love—painting, photography, dance, and so on. Some of these kids are quite consciously emulating the teachers they have met at the School.

#### THE DISTURBED ADOLESCENT

At any one time, the School has among its students at least two who are overtly psychotic, at least five who have been psychotic, and at least fifteen with serious psychoneuroses. About the same number would be classified by more conventional therapists as suffering from "character disorders." Of course most of these kids are creatively talented, so they have also suffered the subtle assaults made by our culture upon creatively talented, more or less "insubordinate" kids who can't and won't live up to their "potential" as measured by IQ tests. They have been pressured by parents and school authorities who see college as the ultimate place into which to maneuver their children so as to feel they have equipped them for the kind of life Daddy lives. All that I have said earlier about the pressures placed upon adolescents in middle-class America applies to both the intact and the disturbed adolescent, but the effect of such pressure on the disturbed can be devastating. If a child has come to feel guilty about his own desires for love and understanding, he may feel even more guilt at "letting Daddy and Mommy down" by performing poorly in school. This is particularly painful to see in the rather common family situation in which the father (like mine) works hard and supports the family superbly from the material point of view, while avoiding confrontation with his unsatisfied and disappointed wife, whom he has long since ceased to love. He stays away from home, and his children have the choice of identifying with him as a passive guarded occasional visitor behind the newspaper or before the TV, making none of the family decisions and sharing nothing important with anyone in the family, or else having little or nothing of Daddy with which to identify. Boys who have mostly mother and little father in the parent department are faced with terrible choices. These are the kids Kenneth Keniston wrote about in *The Uncommitted.* Having no close male to admire and to emulate, they drift from one educational and occupational scene to another, looking for something they can't define and fearing that each situation will reveal the basic terrible secret—that they don't know how to grasp any task and do it effectively, that they can't get pleasure from anything they try to do, because they don't know how. Whatever the particular neurotic problems may be within a particular family, it is a well-known finding in child psychiatry that children tend to blame *themselves* for being unloved or hated or ignored. If a child has been unloved or hated or ignored or seduced or sadistically or masochistically trained in early childhood, at a very deep level he excuses his parents and blames himself. Another very basic truth in child psychiatry is that whatever the nuclear problems have been intrapsychically in the first years of any child's life, they will emerge once again in his life with greatly increased energy when he reaches adolescence. These unsolved problems become once more the focal conflicts behind new neurotic symptoms and character traits. So the boy who has been pushed and molded by an unhappy and unsatisfied mother without a father close enough to teach him male style, will reach adolescence and in some way react to society's demands like those of his mother. Feeling helpless to resist these demands or to channel his own energies into some creative solution to meet them while expressing his own individuality, he flees, drops out, finds that he just "can't perform" in school, in any job, sexually.

An equally common pattern among middle-class disturbed adolescent girls, and hence among the students at the School, is a product of the same family situation working upon the daughters. The father is a relatively small force in this family, and the neurotic unhappy mother dominates the scene. The daughter must decide whether she wants to be like mother, who cannot stand her life as a woman, or to try to be as different from mother as she can. The number of girls at the School who avow, "I'll never be like my mother—I'd rather die!" is very great. But what choice is there? Mother brings daughter up to be like her and conveys her feelings about her woman's life to daughter both consciously and unconsciously. Very frequently these mothers are the kind labeled "unawakened" by women's lib spokeswomen. They are not conscious of the depths of their resentment at being imprisoned as housewives in suburban affluent minimum-security institutions. Life has somehow cheated them, love has gone, work has increased, and they don't even feel the right to express these feelings openly. So the message they give their daughters consciously is, "Grow up to be like me," but unconsciously it is, "I hate my life!" So the daughter who tries to be different finds resistance from her unconsciously jealous mother. The disturbed adolescent girl blames herself for her "misbehavior," her angry feelings, and finds ways to act out her feeling of worthlessness and guilt. She cuts her wrists, overdoses on sleeping pills, gets carelessly pregnant, has an abortion, becomes depressed, commits suicide. It is a commonplace in the literature of psychoanalysis and psychiatry that there are many unconscious reasons why a mother will feel disastrously mixed feelings toward her newborn daughter, and the effects of such covert hatred and jealousy upon the psychic development of the child are well-known.

What I am leading up to is that there *is* a kind of cultural pattern, a style of family life in the suburban American middle class; this style in its variations affects all of the children. When the children are suffering from deep internal conflicts dating from early childhood, these conflicts will certainly surface as symptoms during adolescence. Even when the children are deeply intact, the pressures of our culture upon them are sufficient to bring out symptoms for awhile; this is what Erikson described eloquently in *Childhood and Society* as "identity diffusion." The disturbed adolescents in the School have been exposed to:

1. Deep troubles within their nuclear families early in life —these are going to crystallize as neuroses and "character disorders" unless something is done now, during adolescence.
2. Deep troubles within their nuclear families during their adolescence, both the special problems between father and mother and their other children that existed early in the child's life, *plus* the general problems that afflict the middle-class family in American suburbs today. Here I refer to all the conditions of lack of common goals and closeness, deterioration of religion and values, intrusion of the mass media (dominated by advertising and money hunger) upon the consciousness of all family members, the high rate of loveless marriages, separations and divorces—in short, *all* the alienating factors in our society. These factors will lead to identity diffusion, to enormous difficulty in finding some kind of life that looks like it could be satisfying, unless something is done now, during adolescence.

The disturbed adolescent we see at the School has been hit

hard by *both* sets of factors, both early in life and later. The intact adolescent is being hit hard now, in his adolescence by the second set of factors, the deterioration of unifying principles in the American family of today. Conventional psychotherapy can help the disturbed adolescent with the results of the first set of factors, help him with his neurosis or his character problems. In the years before I had the School, I found myself in the position of most psychotherapists winding up a successful period of therapy with a creative adolescent, saying in effect, "Now you know why you have had the symptoms you came to me for, you're stronger now. Go out and find a life which expresses you!" But so often the patient would try hard, and return saying, "I can't find it." And he would be right; he needed a source of emotional support, a validation of himself and goals during the crucial period of seeking his own life style in the midst of an alienated society. This the School *does* provide. So during and after individual psychotherapy, the disturbed adolescent finds the support he needs at the School, and he "graduates himself" from it when he is ready. The School is a much more intensely therapeutic atmosphere than can be provided by an individual therapist in an hour or two a week. This is why many of the disturbed adolescents who come to the School as veterans of therapy with anywhere from one to six previous therapists, are finally able to make a better life for themselves after involvement in the School. When these patients are seeing me individually as well as participating in the School, I have noticed that individual psychotherapy moves more rapidly. I can see first-hand how the patient relates to other kids, to his teachers, to learning situations. And thus we get down to business more quickly in his therapeutic sessions.

This reminds me of what happened to me when I first began to notice how much more quickly my individual patients were getting better when they joined the School as well. I felt an unaccountable sense of irritation. One day it dawned on me that this was the reaction of the psychoanalytically trained part of my thinking: my patients were getting better before expressing "insights" verbally. Yet they were dealing much better with their families, their peers, and with creative work. There are two possible explanations:

1. This improvement is a "flight into health," by which the patient seems "cured" before he faces his real problems in depth, and thus he avoids facing them. In time the improvement decays.
2. Another explanation: the adolescent who finds himself in a genuinely therapeutic environment at the School is actually getting therapy from his community. This is the old "therapeutic community" idea. The young patient through therapy begins to understand where his conflicts are and how they have blocked his development. He is in an environment in which he can make some tentative attempts to change his unsuccessful style, to be more open, assertive, give more of himself. Unlike the often uncaring and unnoticing school environment at high school or college, unlike the often sabotaging environment of his family, whose members may not love him or are jealous of him, the members of his new extended family at the School notice his attempts at new and better functioning and reward these attempts with recognition and praise. This encourages him to pursue his psychotherapy even more and so on. At the same time, the patient has around him a number of identification figures, his teachers and peers at the School, whose qualities he can emulate. This also accelerates his growth. There is no accident about it; he encounters people at the School who are successful in the very endeavors he pursues himself, and what is more they share their styles and techniques with him as members of his therapy group.

We have not found the money nor the time to pursue a careful statistical study of the lives of our "graduates." Such a follow-up will await some sort of grant for the purpose, if we can get one. But the "graduates" who have come back to visit us have been many, and they do not seem to have regressed. They are generally surer of what they want, more open and honest in dealing with life. By very gross measures, they are not in hospitals, they do not get arrested, they are not in therapy again, as they were before. More subtly, they are more like adults, less like children in coping with life's realities. Maturity accounts for some of this, but in many cases it is clear that they would not have been able to make such strides toward maturity without having found at the School the environment they needed to get them started.

So often psychotherapy with adolescents is hampered by the rut the patient is in—his neurotic family interactions, the inflexible schools insensitive to his needs, the cliques and snobbishness of adolescent peer groups in high schools, prep schools, colleges, neighborhoods. Because of this, improvements through individual psychotherapy often are very hard-won. Having the School which is actually both "family" and peer group as well as school, makes them infinitely easier. I have come to see my two roles, as director of the School and as psychotherapist with its students, as interacting closely. I can rely on my understanding of personality, codified by my psychiatric training, to help me understand what is going on between the students and faculty of the School, while I can relax and trust the intuitive skills of the staff and more advanced students to help others. I can intervene wherever I feel a clarification or an interpretation or a confrontation is needed, whether with students or faculty. As psychotherapist, I can work individually, in depth, upon those problems which must be solved before a student can grow in the environment of the School.

So when Gail announced in one group therapy session, "I

am what I am—but not yet!," I found I was able to say with confidence, "Just stick around the School, Gail, and you surely will be!"

And she did.

# Bibliography

Baba Ram Dass. *Be Here Now.* New York: Crown, 1971.
Bettelheim, Bruno. *Children of the Dream.* New York: Macmillan, 1969.
Coles, Robert, et al. *Drugs and Youth.* New York: Liveright, 1971.
Costy, Alan, ed. *Mass Media and Mass Man.* New York: Holt, Rinehart and Winston, 1968.
Erikson, Erik. *Childhood and Society,* rev. ed. New York: W. W. Norton, 1968.
*Identity: Youth and Crisis.* New York: W. W. Norton, 1968.
Friedenberg, Edgar Z. *Coming of Age in America.* New York: Random House, 1965.
Getzels, J. W. and Jackson, P. W. *Creativity and Intelligence.* New York: Wiley, 1962.
Herrigel, Eugene. *Zen in the Art of Archery.* New York: Pantheon, 1971.
Laing, R. D. *The Politics of Experience.* New York: Pantheon, 1967.
Leonard, George. *Education and Ecstasy.* New York: Delacorte Press, 1968.
Lewis, Oscar. *Five Families.* New York: Basic Books, 1959.
*Children of Sanchez.* New York: Random House, 1961.
*La Vida.* New York: Random House, 1966.

Maslow, Abraham. *Toward a Psychology of Being.* New York: Van Nostrand Reinhold, 1968.

Mead, Margaret. *Culture and Commitment.* New York: Natural History Press, 1970.

Salinger, J. D. *The Catcher in the Rye.* Boston: Little Brown, 1951.

Schneebaum, Tobias. *Keep the River on Your Right.* New York: Grove Press, 1969.

Turnbull, Colin. *The Forest People.* New York: Simon and Schuster, 1961.

Watts, Alan. *The Way of Zen.* New York: Pantheon, 1957.

Wolfe, Tom. *The Pump House Gang.* New York: Farrar, Straus and Giroux, 1968.

*The Electric Kool-Aid Acid Test.* New York: Farrar, Straus and Giroux, 1968.

SHEPARD GINANDES, M.D., has led an extraordinary career as psychiatrist, professional folk singer, sculptor, yoga teacher, professor of psychiatry, and now director of the School We Have. While still in his teens, he cut his first records. He received his M.D. at the Harvard Medical School where he was instructor of psychiatry from 1957 to 1960. He has also been assistant professor of adolescent psychiatry at the Boston University School of Medicine. For the past fifteen years, Dr. Ginandes's professional career has been devoted to working with adolescents: as director of court clinics in Cambridge and Roxbury, as chief of a mental health team assigned to the Hawaii Youth Correctional Program, as chief psychiatric consultant, Massachusetts Department of Youth Service, and as originator and group leader of special seminars at Boston University on drug use, and on ways of reaching alienated, or "dropout" young people. He lives with his wife, who is a dancer, and their four teen-age boys in Concord, Massachusetts.